Dear, Dear Livy

The Story of Mark Twain's Wife

Dear, Dear Livy

The Story of Mark Twain's Wife

by Adrien Stoutenburg
and Laura Nelson Baker

CHARLES SCRIBNER'S SONS

NEW YORK

The acknowledgments for
Dear, Dear Livy appear on pages 185 and 186.

To that stimulating writing teacher
of Minneapolis days

Thomas E. Gaddis

Chapter One

We should have brought skates with us when we came for our walk, Rose," the pretty, dark-haired girl in the blue coat said as the two girls paused beside the frozen pond to watch a group of skaters. She tucked her mittened hands into the sleeves of her coat, to warm her tingling fingers. Even though her coat came below her ankles and her shoes were buttoned close, the cold was penetrating.

The speaker, sixteen-year-old Olivia Langdon, pretended not to notice the glances cast toward her and her friend by some of the older boys when they skated past. It was not dignified or ladylike to encourage boys to stop and talk, although it was all right if they stopped of their own accord.

"I'd love to be out there on the ice." Rose Wilson waltzed around in a small circle on the hard-packed snow where the girls were standing. "If we had our skates, a boy might ask us to skate with him."

"I think I see John Fletcher, whom you think so handsome, coming this way with another boy." Livy dropped her glance, pretending to study the fur on her coat sleeve. "Don't let them see us watching them, Rose."

"No . . . I won't." Rose gave one quick glance at the approaching boys and then she, too, looked at the ground.

"Good afternoon, Miss Livy. Good afternoon, Miss Rose."

Livy glanced up, recognizing the speaker as a boy named Carleton whom she had seen in church. "Good afternoon," she answered politely. "Is the ice smooth?"

The boy, balancing deftly on his skates, nodded. "John and I have been out here nearly two hours."

John, who was looking with obvious admiration at Livy's friend, said, "We came over here to ask you to come out on the ice with us." When Rose said they had not brought skates, he said, "We'll take ours off, and then we can all slide on our boots. The ice is very slick, but Carleton and I will see that you don't fall."

"Would you like to, Livy?" Carleton asked.

Livy hesitated. She did not really know this boy and Papa was strict about her associating with anyone she met in a casual way. Of course she had seen him in church. . . . She said, finally, "I would rather not, thank you, Carleton."

Rose, however, had already consented to go with John Fletcher onto the ice. As Carleton skated off, John sat down on a snowbank and removed his skates, smiling up at Rose and Livy. When he finished, he stood up and took Rose by the arm.

"I don't like to leave you standing here alone, Livy," Rose said, though she was obviously yearning to go off with John.

"Nonsense," Livy said gaily. "If I get cold I'll walk about a bit. I can say over my Latin—I should have been studying it this afternoon, you know."

"Oh, Livy! You can't study out here in the cold!" Rose protested. But a few minutes later, she and her partner were out on the pond, sliding and laughing.

Livy watched them for a few minutes. Rose nearly fell twice, but each time John caught her. How romantic it would be, Livy thought, if Rose and John should fall in love and get married, when they were old enough. Rose would have to let her be a bridesmaid—that is, if she were not married herself by then. Livy certainly hoped to be married—to someone strong and tall and handsome who would save her from every fall, exactly as John was saving Rose from falls on the ice.

Her feet grew a little numb, so Livy began to move about at the edge of the pond, dreaming about the future. Papa said she was too young yet for suitors, but some day she would not be. She would like to marry a man very much like her father, she decided, and settle down to raise a family right here in Elmira. Her husband would not have to be rich, at least not at first. Mama had often told her the story of how Papa had once been a clerk in a grocery store and how he had saved his money and invested it in different things—but mostly in wood and coal—until he became rich enough so that none of them had to worry about money now. I would help my husband to save and plan for the future, Livy thought. She really ought to go over her Latin as she had said she would, but the clear, bright air and the black tree limbs stretched against the sky were too distracting. Perhaps, she thought, even though her shoes were slippery, she could walk out a little way on the ice. It was not as slick-looking here by the edge of the pond as out in the middle where Rose and John were.

Livy found a small area, half-concealed behind some reeds, where the snow had blown off, but on which no one had yet skated. She thrust out her right foot to see just how slippery the ice was, and the foot slipped out from under her. She fell, hitting the ice hard, landing in a sitting position. Seeing that her skirt was caught under her and exposing most of her leg, she reached forward to pull it down before anyone should come— and felt a flashing pain all along her spine! Frightened, she tried to get to her feet, but found it impossible. She managed to call out once and then fainted.

Livy Langdon's fall on the ice and the partial paralysis which followed it brought heartbreak to the Jervis Langdon home in Elmira, New York. The Langdons had two other children. Sue, ten years older than Livy, an adopted but well-loved member of the family, was married to Theodore Crane, who was associated with Mr. Langdon in the coal business. Charles, Livy's brother, was four years younger than she was and a robust, lively personality. The Langdons had been a happy, successful family until the day of the accident.

For two years after her fall on the ice, Livy lay in her large, dim, high-ceilinged bedroom, seeing no one except the members of her family and a procession of doctors Jervis Langdon brought to examine her. Medicines were prescribed and courses of treatment carefully adhered to. She was unable even to sit up in bed. A mechanical lifting apparatus was installed with the hope of raising and lowering her but even with this tackle, sitting up made Livy so nauseated that the anxious family stopped her attempts.

Looking up at the almost-useless tackle one cold winter day, Livy thought in despair, "I'm almost eighteen years old and I shall lie here helpless forever." But she knew that despair was wrong, and she tried to force her mind away from these dark thoughts, closing her eyes and praying in a whisper for God's help. The Langdons were a deeply religious family, and Livy's faith was strong. Guiltily, at the end of her prayer, she added a few extra words asking that she might some day, if she got well, still find the gallant, wonderful man about whom she had been dreaming that day by the pond. He would be strong enough so that when she grew tired, he would pick her up in his arms and carry her as lightly as if she were foam. He would be noble and fine and dedicated to all that was highest and finest in life. And some day, under the elm tree or in the rose arbor, he would ask her to marry him.

There was a knock on her bedroom door, and Livy's father came in.

"Oh, Papa, I didn't hear you come home!" Livy's spirits rose. She loved all the members of her family, but Papa had been, in these two terrible years, her rock of strength and hope. "I'm so glad to see you," she said, holding out both arms to him.

Jervis Langdon put the package he was carrying on Livy's bed and bent over to receive her welcoming kiss. Then he stood back and looked at her. "Is there pain today?" he asked.

"Not much, Papa. The pills are a great help." She smiled up at him. "You always look so handsome when you are dressed for town," she told him. Sometimes she wished that her father would get rid of his muttonchop whiskers, but otherwise Livy thought his strong jaw and sensitive mouth were admirable evidence of his splendid character.

Her father laughed. "For that compliment you deserve a gift." He indicated the package on the bed. "Shall I help you open it?"

Livy let him undo the gay ribbon and remove the shining paper. When a square white box was revealed, she said eagerly, "Let me lift the cover."

Inside was a music box, a delightful one with delicate carvings and lovely colors. "It was made in Switzerland," her father told her. "The moment I saw it I decided that you must have it." He took it from her and wound it. A gay, sweet melody tinkled out across the room.

When Livy had finished examining her gift, her father pulled a chair close to the bed and took her hand in his. "Livy," he said, "I have something to tell you."

His tone was solemn, but Livy looked up at him with trusting dark eyes. Nothing her father could tell her could be any worse than the hard truth she lived with each day of her life.

"Yes, Papa?"

"You know we have tried every doctor who might be able to help you."

"I know." Livy felt a faint alarm. Was her father going to give up hope? If so, then she was lost, because it was Papa, more than anyone, who had helped her to keep up her courage.

"Well, Cousin Andrew thinks we should try Dr. Newton, the famous osteopathic healer who has come to town. There are posters on all the walls telling about the cures he has made." Jervis Langdon frowned as he spoke. To him, the circus atmosphere surrounding the renowned healer was distasteful, but Andrew had convinced him to give the man a try. "I called on Dr. Newton this morning, and he has agreed to come and see you. I have made an appointment for tomorrow."

"How—does this doctor work?" Livy asked timidly. She was so tired of being examined and advised and questioned by medical men. Still, if Papa thought there was hope . . .

"I don't know, my darling. I will have to put you in his hands—except that I will be here, as always, standing guard."

"My dearest Papa." Livy reached out to touch her father's cheek. "I will do whatever you tell me."

The next day the maid came in after breakfast and brushed Livy's hair, parting it in the middle and combing it back behind her ears the way Livy liked it. Dressed in her prettiest nightgown, with soft ruffles at the wrist and throat, Livy waited for the sound of the new doctor's carriage wheels on the driveway outside. A fresh pink flower Charley had brought shyly in to her from the conservatory lay between her fingers as they rested on the satin bedspread. Studying the flower, she tried to remember how the conservatory and the gardens looked in winter. She could easily picture the great elm at the corner of the house, with its arching boughs, and the flock of smaller elms near the coach house, even though the curtains of her room were always drawn and she had not seen the out of doors during the whole two years. But she was beginning to forget just where things were in the gardens.

A small, nervous pulse throbbed in Livy's throat. New doctors always made her uneasy and this one, because he was different, seemed even more alarming to face. But I want to get well, she told herself, so I must try to stay calm and composed. All the doctors said rest and composure were important. In spite of her nervousness, hope flared up in Livy, as it always did at any possibility of being cured. God would answer her prayers —at least He would if it was His plan for her to get well.

There! There were the carriage wheels. Livy strained

her ears but all she could hear was a murmur of voices below and the boom of a clock. Faint yellow light rippled against the other side of the curtains, so the sun must be shining. It was a good omen, Livy thought, on such a wintry day.

There were steps on the staircase, and then the door to her room opened. Her grandmother, her mother, and her father had all come upstairs together with the new doctor.

"Livy, dear, this is Doctor Newton. My daughter Olivia, doctor." Jervis Langdon made the introduction brief.

The doctor greeted Livy and stood looking at her for a minute or two. Finally he turned to Mr. Langdon and said, "I'd like to be alone with your daughter."

Livy's mother and father exchanged glances. Planting his feet firmly on the flowered carpet her father said, "We shall have to stay with her, sir."

The doctor did not argue. He walked to the narrow windows and with a tug, drew back the first of the damask curtains. With another sweep of his hand, the remaining curtain was drawn aside. Then he flung open the window.

Livy sent a wild look toward her father.

"That cold air—" Jervis Langdon began to protest, the skin over his cheekbones tightening, his upper lip beginning to quiver with indignation.

But the doctor was already back at Livy's bedside. He told Livy to try to sit up.

Mrs. Langdon exclaimed, "She can't! She can't sit up even with the help of the tackle. It makes her ill."

Dr. Newton paid no attention to this. He asked Livy again to try to sit up.

She stared up at him, her lips trembling. "I—can't," she said.

"Yes, you can," the osteopath assured her in a kindly but firm voice. "I will help you."

Perspiration stood out on Livy's forehead. Could she do what he asked? She moistened her lips. A cool, sweet current of air moved across the foot of the bed from the open window, and memories of the world she had not seen for so long stirred her profoundly. Sunlight touched the polished chair backs and legs, her dresser, the scroll-work on the music box. If she could sit up, she would be able to see her favorite elm. . . .

"I'll try," she whispered.

She raised her head slowly, groping with one hand for the high bed post and propping an elbow under herself. Pain wrenched her, but she braced herself for the final effort, dampness gathering in the faintly blue hollows under her eyes.

I'm halfway there—if I could get the rest of the way . . . The richness of the thought gave her fresh strength.

She sat up. Dizziness threatened, then receded. She stared at the bright top branches of the ice-coated elm tree glittering in the sunlight. But then the dizziness returned, and she fell back on the bed, closing her eyes.

When she opened them, her father stood over her, the sunlight on his face. "Livy! Oh, Livy!" he said. "You did it. You sat up alone." Tears gleamed in his eyes.

"Now," Dr. Newton said, "we will try something else." Gently pushing Livy's father aside, the doctor told Livy she was to get up and walk a few steps.

At these words, there was a gasp from Livy's mother and her father said, "One miracle a day is enough. After all, doctor, she has been flat on her back for two years."

"Then that's long enough," said the doctor. He bent over Livy once more. "Lean on me. Soon you will not need help, but at first you do. Take a deep breath of that fresh air, and don't be afraid."

Livy slid her legs over the edge of the bed, blushing as the frothy hemline crept up above her ankles. Nausea swirled in her, and the room dipped dangerously. Her ears roared.

"Just a few steps," the doctor insisted. "Just enough so you know you can do it. You must have self-confidence and faith. Believe that you can walk, Miss Langdon, and you will."

Livy stood on her feet, with the doctor's help. The wind and sunlight coming from the windows were like a tonic.

"Take a step. Don't worry. Take just one step."

Shakily, swaying, she thrust one foot ahead of the other.

"Now another," the doctor said.

Carefully she took another step. Then one more.

It was a dream. It could never last. Through the open windows the elm branch was as glossy as a deer's antler. Beyond it were little balls and fluffs of clouds, seeming to prance in the wind that shook the curtains. The wind grew stronger, blasted against her, sent her swaying toward the doctor.

"That's enough." Jervis Langdon sprang to his daughter's side. He swept her up in his arms and carried her to the bed.

Dimly, Livy heard Dr. Newton tell her family that after a little practice she would be able to walk farther, perhaps as far as two hundred yards. Two hundred yards! She closed her eyes against the happiness that swept over her at this glorious hope.

The family, seeing she was exhausted, tiptoed out of the room after the departing doctor, and Livy fell asleep.

Some time later, she woke to the tinkling notes of her music box. Sleepily she turned her head to see her brother Charley standing by her bed, grinning down at her.

"Good for you, Livy," he said huskily.

Chapter Two

The months following Livy's successful attempt to walk again were difficult ones. She was eager to grow strong enough to try longer and longer walks but her will and her physical strength did not match. Her mother and father, used to thinking of her as an invalid, curbed her eagerness. They were worried that she might lose the frail resources of strength she had gained. If it had not been for Dr. Newton's stern warnings, they would have held her back even more than they did. He had left instructions for the course Livy was to follow, emphasizing the importance of fresh air, sunlight, and exercise.

With the coming of spring the following year, 1864, Livy longed to go outdoors. She was eager to visit the conservatory and walk in the gardens, where a few early blooms could now be seen. In a month there would be garden roses. Livy loved roses. Her family had kept bouquets of them in her room while she was ill, but it was not the same as seeing them flower on the bushes.

In April, Livy was to come downstairs for the first

time since her accident. Her sister Susan had returned from the South to her home on East Hill just outside Elmira.

"I want to surprise Sue and Theo when they come here for dinner tonight," Livy told her mother on the morning of the day she was to venture downstairs. "Please don't tell them I'm going to join you all at the table, Mama, or it will spoil my surprise."

"I won't say a word," Mrs. Langdon promised. The two of them were in Livy's room, discussing letters which had come in the morning's mail. "Are you sure you are strong enough, darling? You look flushed."

"If I am flushed," Livy said, "it is from pleasure. I'm getting so much better—and Sue is home—and Alice Hooker is coming to visit. Oh—" She flung her hands out in a gesture of openness and giving. "I'm just happy." She leaned forward and kissed her mother's cheek.

Mrs. Langdon left then and sent in the maid to help Livy dress. Livy, holding a hand mirror in front of her as her hair was being combed, studied her reflection intently. The flush Mama had mentioned was more becoming than the pale cheeks she had lived with so long, she thought. The pinkness made her eyes seem a darker blue, too. She put the mirror down. She did so want to be truly well, she thought, even if she would never be as strong as other girls her age. She was over eighteen now, the age when Rose and Lucy and others of her friends had beaux who were permitted to call on them. But Mama and Papa had explained to Livy that it would not be right for her to receive such callers, since she would never be strong enough to be a healthy wife to any man. Livy was resigned to this, wistful though she often felt when her friends told her of their dances and parties. Lucy was already betrothed, although there would be no marriage until this dreadful war was over, because her fiancé was with General Grant in Mississippi. He was only nineteen years old, but he had already seen hundreds of men killed, Lucy said.

Livy tried to put the war out of her mind, as her father wanted her to do. "Leave it to President Lincoln," he said. "Lincoln—and General Grant."

The war was going better than it had. Everyone said that Grant was a brilliant general. He was pushing steadily southward, and the President had expressed great hope for an early victory by the North. Only it took too long, Livy thought, and there was too much suffering on both sides.

"There, Miss Livy." The maid handed Livy a pink sacque, or jacket, to wear over her dress, in case there were any drafts in the house. Livy was ready to take her morning promenade, first to the door of her room and then down the hall and into her mother's room, resting there for a time until she ventured back to her own room once more. Later in the day, she would take a second stroll over the same territory, and tonight, tonight, Papa would carry her downstairs! It seemed as exciting as a picnic by the river would have been, before her accident.

Sue arrived around four o'clock. "Theo is coming home with Papa," she explained to Livy, "when they are through for the day." She seated herself on the foot of Livy's bed, tucking her foot up under her skirts and looking her younger sister over carefully. "I had the carriage bring me straight here instead of going around to wait for Theo and Papa, so you and I could have a visit. I feel as if we hadn't really seen each other since I got back."

"Tell me about the country," Livy said. "I am so eager to see it. And I will, soon."

Sue obligingly described the freshness of the hills near her farm home, of the trees' new greenness, the young calves and colts capering behind their mothers in the pastures. Quarry Farm, as the place was called, had long been a favorite week-end spot for the Langdons. Now it belonged to Sue and Theo, a gift from Mr. Langdon.

"Now," Sue said, "you tell me about you, Livy. Are you getting along with your reading? The last time we talked of it, you were learning lines from Mr. Holmes."

Livy picked up the book which lay on her bedspread. "I do still like Mr. Holmes," she said. She had copied parts of *The Autocrat of the Breakfast Table* into her diary. "He seems to me so wise in his statements. But a friend sent me this little book the other day. It's by a Mr. Whitman."

"Do you like it?" Sue picked up the volume and read the title aloud. "*Leaves of Grass.* A lovely title."

Livy looked out the window a moment. "I cannot

honestly say I like the book. Some of it seems to me in very poor taste. But sometimes—well, there is a line about grass being the handkerchief of the Lord. That seems very beautiful to me. There are other beautiful images in it, too."

"I have heard of Mr. Whitman." Sue Crane leafed through the volume. "Mr. Emerson thinks Whitman is a great poet. And Theo says that Mr. Whitman has been nursing the soldiers during the war, going into the front lines." She put the book back down on Livy's bed.

"I'll come up to see you again after dinner," she said, "and Theo will, too. They are having a problem with one of the men at the plant. He has a large family and says that he needs more wages if he is to support them. But Papa and Theo do not think he is worth more wages. Still, as Papa says, there are all those mouths to feed." Sue sighed. "I leave it to Papa and Theo, except that I told them I should like for us to take milk and butter from the farm to those children, if it would not give offense."

"Sue, you are so tender-hearted!" Livy exclaimed. "You would give away your last penny."

"So would you," Sue said. She got off the bed again and stood up. "Everybody in this family is kind. Even Charley, in spite of his boisterous ways. He keeps talking about how Papa ought to let him go into the army; he thinks he could pass for older than he is."

"Oh!" Livy was shocked. "I could never bear to think of Charley down there in all that dreadful mud, with flies and mosquitoes and disease. Lucy says Roscoe writes of walking through swamp mud up to his knees."

"It's in a good cause," Sue said. Her face shadowed. "When I think of all those slaves—I saw some of them once, when Papa was helping with the underground. They were so ragged and thin and looked so frightened."

"I know. Mama told me."

When Sue had gone back downstairs, Livy found herself thinking again about the War Between the States. Long before Fort Sumter had surrendered and it had become generally accepted that there would be war within the United States, her father had declared that slavery would have to go. "Men are not animals, to be slaves to one another," he had said. "It goes against the grain when human beings are treated worse than we treat our horses."

That was why Papa had given money to help the runaway slaves when they came through Elmira. Some people said that there was a tunnel under Elmira College that was used as an underground depot for the slaves. If there was such a tunnel, Livy had never seen it during the few months she had attended the college before her accident.

At seven o'clock Livy's father came up to get her and carried her down the wide mahogany staircase in his arms. At the foot of the stairs he set her gently down and offered her his arm so she could walk into the dining room. The family were already seated around the table. Livy could hear their voices and laughter from where she stood clinging to the newel post, out of sight of the diners.

"Take my arm, darling. We'll walk in together," Jervis Langdon said. "I excused myself from the table by telling the family I had to see Emil before he left for the evening." Emil was the Langdon family coachman. Mr. Langdon smiled at his daughter. "It was not a lie. I did go out to speak to Emil, before I came upstairs."

"You never lie, Papa." Her father was known for his high principles, not only in Elmira but in other places where he had business interests. "I think I would like to walk in by myself. I have been resting all afternoon —and it will make so much more of an impression if I walk in without help."

"If you're sure you are strong enough—"

"I am sure." Livy let go of the post and started in the direction of the voices. It was truly wonderful to think that perhaps, after this, she would be taking all her dinners with her beloved family. Two and a half years of eating from trays, of being fed only selected foods chosen to build up her strength, of taking tonic after tonic, had taken away most of her interest in food. But tonight she was hungry. She wanted to taste everything that was on the table.

Jervis Langdon hung back, letting his daughter make her grand entrance alone. It was a great moment for Livy and he did not want to spoil it.

Charley was the first to catch sight of his sister.

"Livy!" he yelled, bouncing up from his place and rushing to her. "Why didn't you tell me that you wanted to come downstairs? I would have carried you!"

Livy put her hand on her brother's coat sleeve. "Dear Charley," she said softly. She didn't weigh very much, but Charley would have found her weight more than he could handle, all the same. She said, "Papa carried me. I only walked from the hall." She had planned to walk all the way to the table but something in her brother's face made her change her mind. "If you will let me take your arm now, though, I would be grateful," she said. "That way I won't get as tired."

"You never told me, when I was talking to you this afternoon, that you were coming down!" Sue accused, when the butler had come in and set a place for Livy at the table.

A bouquet of hyacinths and crocuses gleamed blue in the light from the candles that graced the table. The silver soup tureen the butler had just brought in had a sheen that caught bits of light from the candles, and overhead the crystal chandelier swayed very slightly in the breeze from the open window. Everything was as it had been before she had the accident, Livy thought with a deep feeling of gratitude.

She waited until her father and Charley had resumed their places and the servants had returned to the kitchen. Then she said, with a shy, apologetic smile, "I know you must have said grace before I came, but could we all say it together, once more?"

No one spoke for a moment. Then Jervis Langdon cleared his throat and asked for the blessing of God on his table and those loved ones who sat around it and shared its bounty.

Livy, feeling tears prick her eyelids, bent her head. When she raised it again, she saw that there were tears in her mother's and sister's eyes, also. Tears of love and gratitude and happiness.

Chapter Three

$\mathcal{D}$uring the next few years, Livy's health continued to improve. She walked the two hundred yards Dr. Newton had promised, and more. She also began to take part in social activities, watched carefully by her family.

After the Civil War ended in 1865 and the surviving soldiers returned home to Elmira, grateful friends and families feted them. The Langdons did their share of this entertaining, although Jervis Langdon sometimes remarked what a sad contrast the happiness of the North was to the bitterness of the defeated South. The citizens of Elmira had a chance to see this bitterness close at hand, because a prison for captured Confederate soldiers had been opened there toward the end of the war. Livy shivered whenever she caught a glimpse of the grim barracks. The Southern States had been wrong in wanting to secede but they had believed themselves to be right. It seemed terrible to her that men had to be imprisoned for doing what they thought was right.

Livy, delicate though she was both in appearance and fact, attracted suitors. Some of the young men who came to the Langdon parties found the contrast of her fair skin and dark eyes and hair very appealing. They were drawn to Livy by the sweetness of her expression and the intelligence displayed in her conversation. A few called at the Langdon home and hinted their interest to Mr. Langdon.

Jervis Langdon courteously let these young men know that his daughter's hand was not to be had by anyone. Livy had accepted her parents' decision that she would never be strong enough to risk rearing a family.

To compensate, Jervis Langdon escorted Livy and the rest of his family to all the cultural events he could. Livy was very interested in books and plays, lectures and music, and her father saw to it that she had an opportunity to go to New York City for all events of importance in the field of the arts.

Early in 1867, Livy's brother Charley, now eighteen, had gone off on a sea voyage to the Holy Land. The family, worried about some of the high-spirited young man's youthful escapades, felt that a trip in the company of missionaries and pilgrims, such as most of the passengers of *The Quaker City* were supposed to be, would help Charley settle down.

Charley, however, managed to find some ship companions who were not missionaries. One of these was the newspaper correspondent who called himself Mark Twain. Charley lost his head over this passenger fourteen years his senior and could talk of nothing else when he returned from his trip. Until then, the Langdons' knowledge of Twain was that he had got his start in the wild gold and silver rush in California and Nevada and that besides his newspaper letters, he had written *The Jumping Frog,* and it was making him famous.

The December following Charley's return from abroad, the Langdons were spending the Christmas holidays in New York City. Mr. Langdon engaged rooms at the St. Nicholas Hotel and bought tickets for a reading to be given by Charles Dickens early in January, at Steinway Hall.

Two days after Christmas, Charley Langdon burst into the family suite at the hotel and announced that his remarkable friend from *The Quaker City* was in the hotel lobby. Mr. Samuel Langhorne Clemens, known as Mark Twain, wished to pay his respects to Charles's family.

"It's you he really wants to meet, Livy," Charley teased his sister. "I showed him your picture when we were on the boat and I thought he would never get done looking at it."

Livy felt the warm color flood her throat. She never grew used to her brother's teasing. "You should not have done that," she scolded him. Then after a minute, "Anyway, I'm sure you are making it up. Mr. Clemens is a famous man. He could not be interested in meeting a nobody like me."

"Tell him to come up, Charley," Mrs. Langdon said. "We don't wish to be ungracious to someone who was a friend to you when you were so far from home."

A few minutes later, Livy looked up from the book she was reading to see her brother usher in a striking-looking gentleman with curly russet hair and bright blue-green eyes flashing under thick brows. Mr. Clemens looked nothing like any of the young men around Elmira, she thought, studying him from under her lashes. But then he was not a young man. Charley said he was over thirty years old.

"Very kind of you to see me, ma'am," Sam Clemens said to Mrs. Langdon. "And you, sir," he bowed to Mr. Langdon. "And Miss Langdon." He bowed deepest of all in Livy's direction.

They asked him to sit down and everyone talked about the voyage Mr. Clemens and Charley had made to the Holy Land. Then the visitor left, saying that he hoped to see them all again before they returned to Elmira.

"Well, what did you think?" Charley asked of his family. "Isn't he something special? Or maybe you don't see it right off. But wait until you hear him spin one of his yarns." Charley's eyes glinted. "Of course, I wouldn't want him to tell all of the stories he told us on the ship. Some of them would not be fit for Mama and Livy to hear."

"I'm not sure Mr. Clemens is a good friend for you to have, Charley," his father said. "He may be a very brilliant writer but that does not mean he is stable and of good character."

Livy said timidly, "I thought he had a most pleasing

voice, Papa. It was not like anyone else's that I know."

Her father smiled at her. "To tell the truth, I liked the man. Charley, see if Mr. Clemens would like to join us for the Dickens performance next week. And ask him to come here for dinner first."

"I'll be happy to!" Charley went off at once to try to catch up with his friend.

Livy saw Mark Twain again, however, before the evening of the Dickens reading. One of her married friends, a Mrs. Berry, gave a reception on New Year's Day. Livy, in the receiving line, was the first to catch sight of Mr. Clemens' bright head as he followed her brother into the Berry drawing room. A quiver of excitement ran through her. Had Charley really showed Mr. Clemens that ivory miniature of her? Had he admired it? She pushed away her excitement. It was hardly likely, and even if it should happen to be true, what did it matter? No admirer could ever be anything closer than friend to Livy Langdon, and this rough diamond, as Theo Crane had called him, was out of the question. He was a man of the world, ten years older than she was.

Nevertheless, as Sam Clemens stopped beside her and asked in his soft drawl, "How are you, Miss Langdon?" Livy found her cheeks warming. It was with difficulty that she was able to answer. "I am very well, thank you, Mr. Clemens." At that moment she was.

Livy expected that Mr. Clemens would join Charley

and some young ladies at the other side of the room, but he did not. He stood quietly beside her, talking of the Dickens performance which they were to see and asking her if she liked Dickens' novels. Livy's hostess nodded to her that she should take Mr. Clemens to a sofa and offer him some tea, so they walked together to the table where the tea service was and, taking their cups, found a small sofa where they could sit down and continue their conversation.

Later, Mrs. Berry said to Livy, "Is Mr. Clemens as funny when he talks as he is on paper?"

"No . . ." Mr. Clemens had not been humorous at all; they had talked of very serious subjects. Livy could not remember ever having talked before to any man except Papa about such serious subjects.

Livy's muff glistened from the crystals of snow which were melting on it in the warmth of Steinway Hall. On the stage, under a red upholstered structure resembling a shed, stood the English author Charles Dickens, a red flower in his buttonhole. Behind the slant of the crimson shed was a row of lights that made the stage and Mr. Dickens seem to be aflame. Livy thought her face probably matched the scene below, if the excitement she felt was showing on her cheeks.

Her elbow grazed that of her escort and she murmured an apology, but was too shy to look directly at Mr. Clemens. She had not expected that her father's guest would be seated between her and Charley.

"It seems warm," Mr. Clemens said in a low tone just as Mr. Dickens was about to start reading. "May I help you remove your coat, Miss Langdon?"

Livy had to look at him then, noticing for the first time the hawklike thrust of his nose. He was not handsome, she decided, but she liked the quick, sensitive hands which were lifting her coat from her shoulders and she thought that Mr. Clemens had an air of distinction and vitality that set him apart from other men.

Taking a small fan out of her porte-monnaie, she began waving it in front of her face, wondering if it was really as warm in the hall as she felt it was. She concentrated on Mr. Dickens; *David Copperfield* was one of her favorite books.

As Livy listened to familiar lines, tears came to her eyes. Glancing at Mr. Clemens, she saw that he, too, was caught up in the performance. He was leaning forward and his hands had stopped their restless movements. Charley had said that his friend's hands were usually busy with a cigar. Or even, sometimes, a glass of whiskey! Livy found it hard to believe. Mr. Clemens certainly looked like a gentleman—oh, there was some casualness in the way his tie was caught around his collar, and his coat was perhaps not as well-cut as her father's, but his linen was so white it was dazzling.

Sam Clemens turned and smiled at her. "Are you enjoying yourself, Miss Langdon?"

She nodded, overwhelmed by the tenderness of the look which accompanied his question.

They turned back to the stage but now Livy was very

aware of her companion. He was no longer concentrating on the performance. His hand tapped his knee restlessly. Livy thought, half-amused, half-indignant, "Why, I believe he thinks he could do as well as Mr. Dickens!"

When the performance ended, Mr. Langdon came to Livy's side. Sam Clemens thanked him for asking him to join their party and the Langdons prepared to leave. But as Livy turned away on her father's arm, the vibrant, drawling voice said, "I thank you and Charley for your invitation to visit Elmira. I'll be there, the first chance I have."

"You have a standing invitation, Mr. Clemens," Livy's father said warmly.

Papa must have taken a great liking to Mr. Clemens, Livy thought. There was certainly much that was admirable about him, in spite of some odd mannerisms and his colloquial speech. A gentleman, a real one, the most complete one she had ever met, that was Mr. Clemens.

Back at the St. Nicholas, Livy lay looking through the window and listening to the sounds of the city night, after she was in bed. "A genius," Charley had said of Mr. Clemens. Perhaps. He looked like one. What would she do and say if he did come to visit them in Elmira? But he probably would never come. She was not likely to meet Mr. Samuel Clemens again.

From another window in the same city, Sam Clemens saw the shadowy hulk of the St. Nicholas Hotel rising

on the west side of Broadway. The hotel was one of the
show places of the day, a gathering place for million-
aires like the Langdons. Only a few of the windows in
the St. Nicholas were still lighted. He chose one of
them and decided it was Livy's. She was probably looking into a mirror while someone brushed that lovely
dark hair. He would be lucky ever to touch one tress.
She was a saint, while he . . .

He glanced at the cigar in his fingers. At the Berrys',
out of respect for Livy and the other ladies, he had fore-
gone smoking. Well, it had been a small sacrifice. There
was nothing he would not give up for her sake—or
nothing within reason. Even so, how could he hope to
win her?

The window light he had chosen as hers, blinked out.
He felt bereft, as though she had seen through the dark-
ness to his wild, dreaming thoughts and had blown out
the light on purpose. But she would never be so cruel.
Never had he seen a sweeter face, or such dark eyes
changing to glowing blue when she smiled, and never
had he heard such delightful laughter as that which
bubbled up out of that slim throat.

His cigar ash fell, spilling across his waist. He brushed
at the ash ruefully, a small rage at himself growing. He
was a jackass, and worse. A whole list of self-derogatory
names occurred to him, names and words he would
never dare breathe in Miss Langdon's presence.

Sam removed his tie and flung it on the bed. He took
off his shoes and kicked them under a chair—then, on

second thought, he picked them up and stood them neatly side by side. He would have to reform, late in the day though it was. He had a vision of all his old friends back in Virginia City and San Francisco, or home in Hannibal, Missouri, laughing at him for being trapped by a woman at last.

Sam turned to the window again, opened it, and inhaled the cold night air. For all that he might joke about women spoiling a man's fun and taking away his freedom, a good, loving woman was the noblest creation on earth. And the noblest and most beautiful of them was Olivia Louise Langdon.

The light in the far-off hotel window flickered up and then glowed into brilliance again. He smiled.

Chapter Four

*I*t was only August but a few autumn leaves drifted down past the window of the Langdon library. Livy's cousin from Illinois, Hattie Lewis, was visiting her, and the two young women were waiting for Sam Clemens' first visit to Elmira.

"Don't you feel nervous, Livy?" Hattie asked. "I do. I've never entertained a writer before. Of course, you've met him."

"That was months ago," Livy said. "But there's nothing to be nervous about." She put aside the embroidery she had been pretending to do, glad that her cousin could not hear the beating of her heart. "Mr. Clemens is coming to visit Charley. We shan't see much of him, you know."

"Shall I prod you, Livy, so you'll know when to laugh at his jokes? You are such a literal-minded little thing—and his humor is supposed to be of the exaggerated and audacious sort."

"He is sometimes too mocking," Livy said with severity. She had not liked Mr. Clemens' poking fun at

Charles Dickens, as he had in a newspaper after the night at Steinway Hall.

The library door opened and Charley thrust his head in. "What are you two all dressed up for?"

Hattie glanced with attempted disdain at her silk dress. "We're not dressed up."

Livy, feeling suddenly self-conscious in her dark brown "special" velvet, said defensively, "We are only trying to look respectable for Mr. Clemens."

"You'll have to put on your fanciest nightgowns, then. He won't get here until the middle-of-the-night local arrives."

Hattie giggled, but the idea of meeting Sam Clemens in her nightgown shocked Livy. "Well," she said, denying her disappointment at Charley's news, "Hattie and I can go for a ride, then, and not concern ourselves."

Hattie looked at her. "The ride would be more exciting if Mr. Clemens were here to go with us," she said.

A sly sparkle showed in Livy's eyes. "Too much excitement is bad for the heart, Hattie."

Hattie, laughing, decided that perhaps her demure and dainty cousin had a better sense of humor than she had thought.

Livy did not sleep well that night. She listened for a time to the autumn wind crooning softly through the gables and chimneys, dozing off at last to dream that Sam Clemens was riding up to the house. He had a wide-brimmed hat on his curly head, his shoulders and chest were enclosed in what seemed to be a knight's armor.

The sound of a faint scraping noise awakened her. Hearing cart wheels, she raised herself on an elbow, listening. From the courtyard came her brother's smothered laugh and a chuckle she felt sure she recognized.

Livy pushed her feet into slippers and, pulling her dressing gown around her, went to the window. The gas light in its standard at the side of the yard was ablaze, revealing Charley and the person with him.

Livy stared. *That* couldn't be Mr. Clemens in the flapping, bulky, yellow duster, a crumpled and dirty straw hat on his head! As Charley steered his companion toward the house, light struck them. Livy recognized the hawkish nose and the laugh-line creasing one cheek. It was Samuel Clemens.

". . . don't worry," the slow, easy voice drifted up to her. "I've a new set of duds in my valise."

He had better! Livy thought. She was glad that she and Hattie had not waited for hours, dressed in their best, to welcome him.

The door below closed, and she saw the coachman go to extinguish the yard light. She crept back to bed, puzzled. The papers said that Mark Twain dressed like a dandy. But she had also heard that he sometimes liked to wear outrageous clothes, just to shock people.

Whatever he wears tomorrow, Livy decided, I'll take no notice. It was probably logical to wear a duster on the train. The cinders and soot could be terrible. And

Mr. Clemens was a very busy man. Since she had seen him at the beginning of the year, he had been way out to California and back, Charley said, checking on newspaper material he wanted for his new book, *The Innocents Abroad*. He had also been giving humorous lectures.

Livy's mood softened, changing to concern. With no one to look after him, away from his mother and sister most of the time, and with no wife to see to it that he kept proper hours or ate as he should, he was more to be sympathized with than censored.

Even if Livy had determined to be disapproving of the visitor, her determination would not have lasted long in the face of his gaiety and attentiveness during the following week. By the end of the week, she felt as if she had known him for years.

Saturday evening Hattie, who had accompanied Sam and Livy on walks and rides during the week, watched Sam turn the pages of a song book as Livy played the piano. The lamplight shone down on their absorbed faces; Sam's, especially, was revealing. Mr. Clemens, Hattie said to herself, was head over heels in love with Livy.

Sue Crane also guessed the truth as she watched the pair at the piano, but Livy's parents seemed unaware of any designs their guest might have on their treasured daughter. Jervis Langdon's immediate liking for Sam had increased while the well-known writer was a guest in his house.

"Give Sam a turn, Livy," Charley Langdon called out. "I want to hear some of the spirituals he sang for us on *The Quaker City*."

"I don't play the piano," Sam protested. "I just torment it."

But Livy had already moved from the round piano stool. "Do play, please," she said, her eyes both beseeching and encouraging.

Unable to resist Livy, Sam Clemens, with exaggerated flourishes, pretended to inspect the keys, the stool, and even the inside mechanism of the instrument, before he began to play. He had a curious way of attacking the keys, his fingers stretched straight out, so that each time they landed and struck a harmonious chord it seemed a miracle. Livy, standing at one side, looked tense and nervous, as if any success or failure of his was as important as her own.

Sam cleared his throat several times, then leaned his head back, his eyes on the ceiling. He sang—broke off and said something under his breath—and began again.

This time there was no hesitation, the words of the song ringing out loud and clear in his sweet tenor. The room grew very quiet.

> "My Lord He call me!
> He call me by the thunder! . . ."

At the rear of the room, a fire of hickory logs crackled in the fireplace. Outside, there was the vast stillness of stars. Sam's voice echoed and circled the room, so intensely alive that it seemed to take up all the space. He paused only when he missed a chord or had forgotten the words, singing the Negro songs he had learned as a boy in Missouri: "Swing Low, Sweet Chariot"—"Go Chain the Lion Down."

Suddenly he stopped singing. "You have all suffered enough," he said.

"Oh, that isn't so, Mr. Clemens," Livy protested, the song he had sung so movingly still ringing in her ears.

He looked embarrassed, and for once failed to give a jesting answer.

In Livy's room later that night, Hattie said, "Livy, I think I'd better make that trip to New York after all. I only postponed it because Mr. Clemens was coming, but now . . ."

"But now what, Hattie?"

Hattie rubbed rose water over her hands and wrists. "I don't want to be an interference." At Livy's wide-eyed look, she added, "Can't you see that Sam Clemens has got his cap set for you?"

Crimson stained Livy's cheeks. "Why, Hattie Lewis! I'm sure he's never thought of such a thing. Oh, I wish you hadn't said it. If it were true—which it isn't—well, it couldn't be. Mama would have a stroke."

"It's true just the same."

Livy put her hands over her ears. "He doesn't even go to church, any church."

"He will, if he can get you to go down the aisle to the strains of a wedding march." Hattie moved closer to her cousin, feeling suddenly so much older and wiser that she clasped both of Livy's hands in hers. "Promise me that when he asks you to marry him—yes, I know he will. He'll be here another week. I heard your father and Charley urging him. Promise me that when he asks, you'll say Yes."

Livy pulled one hand free and held it to her cheek. Her hair, loosened from its braids, hung down around her shoulders as it used to do so often when she was an invalid. She looked around her at the familiar room. "I could never be happy—or feel safe—anywhere but here," she said.

Hattie said only, "Well, don't close your mind to him—anyone can see that you haven't closed your heart."

Livy looked at her and said gravely, "I don't like the name Samuel."

Hattie could not restrain a giggle. "Oh, Livy! If that's all that stands in the way, you might as well start sending out wedding invitations now."

Chapter Five

*H*er cousin's warning about Mr. Clemens' intentions made Livy self-conscious during the remainder of his visit to Elmira. She was torn between the desire to hear from his own lips that he admired her and the dread of refusing him if he should suggest marriage.

With Hattie gone to New York during the second week of the visit, Livy and Sam found themselves more often alone. The first week they had been a threesome, or sometimes a foursome when Charley was available.

"That brother of yours is quite a buck," Sam said appreciatively to Livy one morning after Charley had excused himself from their company to go and exercise his favorite team of fast-stepping horses.

"Charley does seem a bit wild," Livy said earnestly, "but he is good and kind and he will settle down soon. Papa is very anxious for him to learn to manage the coal company's affairs—Papa says he cannot live forever." Livy smiled at Sam. "I'm sure Papa will live a long time, though. He is very strong."

"Let's go out into the garden," Sam said.

"There is not much bloom left there now," Livy said,

but she accepted the arm he offered. "Perhaps a few chrysanthemums . . ."

They strolled slowly through the hall and out into the open air, Sam urging Livy to lean on him as though he were her father. "I may not be as strong as your father, but I can easily support a little girl like you, Miss Livy," he said.

Livy glanced at him and then glanced away, coloring. He probably had not meant anything at all by his remark, although it seemed to have a double meaning.

It was early September now and the skies had a wintry look, even though the sun shone. The rose bushes had seed pods and the cosmos had only a few blooms left. The gardener was busy removing the more tender plants to the shelter of the glass hothouse. Livy asked him about the health of his child. Then she and Sam walked along the paths through a labyrinth of boxwood.

"Livy Langdon, I do believe you are the most gracious and thoughtful human being I have ever known," Sam said suddenly, putting gentle hands on her shoulders to stop her progress and make her look at him. "I have spent many hours planning just how I would express my feelings about you and how I would put them into such wonderful language that you couldn't resist, but now—" He stopped speaking and dropped his hands from her shoulders. "Livy, I love you very much. You are beautiful and kind and charming and everything else that is lovely and good. Will you do me the honor of becoming my wife?"

It was said, just as Hattie had predicted. Despite the warning, Livy felt the color rising to her cheeks, felt her tongue sticking to the roof of her mouth.

"I—I—why, Mr. Clemens, I never dreamed . . . But, though you are doing me a very great honor, I must tell you—" In despair, Livy looked away from him and out over the garden. "I cannot marry you, Mr. Clemens. I really cannot. I beg you to understand that although I honor you more than any man I have ever met, I cannot marry you." Recovering her composure, she turned again toward the house. "Shall we go back inside?" she asked.

"One minute, please, Miss Livy. Don't turn away from me so quickly. I respect your decision, and I will honor it. But may I ask one favor? No, on second thought, two." Sam reached for her hand this time, clasping the small fingers tightly in his own. "Your friendship means a great deal to me. I don't want to lose it just because I rushed heedlessly into the matter which lies so close to my heart. If you cannot be my wife, then be my sister. Write to me sometimes, as you would to Charley."

"Oh, I will, Mr. Clemens, I will." She could not refuse such a request, Livy thought. The warm clasp of his hand on hers was so strong and reassuring that she let her fingers lie there a few moments. It was not the clasp of a lover, she told herself; it was the clasp of a loving friend. Her eyes gazed earnestly into his as she promised to consider herself his sister, to write to him as such. She felt a great relief at the thought that she would not have to shut this wonderfully stimulating personality out of her life altogether.

When Livy told her parents what had happened, they approved of her behavior.

"I am greatly surprised," Mrs. Langdon said, "that he should have spoken to you about marriage, however, without having consulted your father. This was not properly done—but Mr. Clemens is perhaps not aware of the proprieties."

Before Sam Clemens left the Langdon home that week, he wrote Livy a long letter, telling her how much he appreciated the consideration and kindness she and everyone in the family had shown him. In the letter he told her again that he loved her and always would, and though he accepted her decision, it was very hard for him to do so. He wrote: "It is better to have loved and lost you than that my life should have remained forever the blank it was before." It was an extravagant letter, from a man who was not used to outpourings of emotion and only one paragraph shows a trace of the wit so characteristic of Mark Twain. "Write me *something* from time to time—texts from the New Testament, if nothing else occurs to you—or dissertations on smoking —or extracts from your Book of Sermons—*anything, whatever* . . ."

The next day, Sam Clemens left Elmira for Cleveland. He went from Cleveland to St. Louis, to visit his own family.

He wrote Livy that, if the Langdons were willing, he would like to pay them another visit. He addressed her as his "honored sister." He said that his plan, if she approved, was to spend a day and a night in Elmira, around the twenty-eighth of September.

He actually arrived in Elmira on September 29. Livy, waiting for him to arrive, walked about her room or sat at the piano practicing, wondering nervously if her letters had been too warm and friendly. Would he propose again? And if he did, would it be easier to say No?

Sam Clemens did not propose again. In fact, his visit passed so swiftly that Livy felt she had scarcely seen him before it was time for him to leave. As Charley and Mr. Clemens climbed into a democrat wagon outside the Langdon gate, Livy and her parents, with Sue and Theo, watched from the front porch, waving farewells.

Barney, a new coachman, touched his whip to the horse too smartly. The horse suddenly sprang forward. The two men abruptly hurtled backward over the wagon's stern, Charley's cigar making a flaming arc through the air.

All the Langdons ran to where Charley and the visitor sprawled on the cobblestones. Charley scrambled to his feet, despite some bruises, but Mr. Clemens, Livy saw with anxiety, lay still, his head against the stones.

"Oh, dear!" She clasped her hands together without knowing she did so. Her father, Theo, and Charley all bent over Sam. "Is he—badly hurt?" Livy asked.

At the sound of her voice, Mr. Clemens' eyes opened and looked up at her. A peculiar expression crossed his face and the next minute he slumped into a faint.

"Grab his heels there, Charley," Mr. Langdon commanded. "I'll take his shoulders— Theo, you get in the middle."

Sweating, Charley staggered toward the house with his part of the burden, insisting that he was all right despite his bruises. "Clemens is a dead weight, though. I don't know how a man no bigger than he is can be so heavy."

"Send Barney for the doctor. Mr. Clemens may have concussion." It was Mrs. Langdon who spoke.

The coachman was dispatched and they carried Sam into the Langdon parlor where he revived enough to be able to sit in an armchair. Livy, feeling worried but useless, watched while her sister Sue began to massage liniment into Mr. Clemens' scalp.

"Do you feel pain anywhere?" Sue asked the patient, rubbing vigorously.

"Just from the pain-killer, ma'am," Sam said, wincing.

Livy felt relieved. As long as Mr. Clemens could joke about it, there couldn't be too much wrong. At the sound of her sigh, Sam turned toward her. He looked thoughtful, then groaned.

"I'm afraid the pain's coming back." He lifted a hand and touched his head tenderly. "But, now, don't make a fuss—I can bear it." He made a move as if to stand up, then sank back into the chair again.

"You sit right there, sir," Mr. Langdon ordered, "until the doctor comes."

Sue went on massaging the pain-killer into Sam's fleecy scalp. Her husband said, "You look tired, Sue. Let Livy do that for awhile."

Timidity overwhelmed Livy briefly as she thought about thrusting her hands into the russet curls. But this was no time for shyness. She took the bottle and began to massage Mr. Clemens' head, her fingers tingling as they touched the thick, beautiful hair. How silken and clean it felt. Her fingers probed deeper, seeking for bumps or wounds. "If I hurt you, please tell me," she said.

"No, no—keep on, Miss Livy. I—feel a little better now. Only, don't stop."

When the doctor came and had examined the patient, he looked mystified. "There seem to be no lumps or contusions. My advice to you, Mr. Clemens, is to go to bed and forget it. I'm quite sure you will be all right in the morning."

"Unless there are internal injuries—" Sam said.

Livy, horrified at this thought, excused herself and left the room. If anything should happen to him . . .

Sam grew no worse, but he required three days for

his convalescence. Exercise, he told Livy, was helpful,
especially walking slowly over the leaf-strewn paths
with her. After the walks, they rested in the library and
Livy read to Sam.

Several times she looked up from her reading to find
his gaze on her, intense, tender, and faintly triumphant.
Although he still addressed her as his sister and did not
press his suit openly, Livy felt a growing suspicion. For
a man who had presumably suffered so much pain at
the time of the accident, Mr. Clemens appeared to be in
radiant health.

Sue Crane put her suspicions into words. "Just between you and me, Livy dear," she said shortly after
Sam and his trunk had been carried off, safely this time,
in the wagon, "I don't think he was hurt by his fall at
all. I think he deliberately feigned his injuries in order
to spend more time here with you."

Livy attempted an indignant denial but gave up. Both
she and Sue burst into laughter. She ought to have been
angry at her suitor, Livy thought, because it had been
outright deceit. No, mischief. Mr. Sam Clemens, for all
that he was thirty-three years old and a celebrity,
seemed to her like a lovable, unpredictable child. He
would never grow old.

His name should not be Samuel. It should be Youth.
That was what she would call him if ever—

Livy avoided the searching look Sue gave her, but it
was no use.

"Has he asked you again?" Sue wanted to know.

"No. I doubt that he will. In any case, I shall have to answer as before."

Both of them were keenly aware of the lack of conviction in Livy's voice, despite her firm words.

Chapter Six

ℒivy's room was gloomy in the October rain but her thoughts were bright. In her dress pocket was Mr. Clemens' last letter to her, from Hartford, Connecticut. He had made a wonderful friend, he said, a minister, the Reverend J. H. Twichell. Oh, Mr. Clemens was indeed changing his life, Livy thought, as he had promised his beloved "sister" he would try to do. His letter had described how he had gone with this Mr. Twichell to an institution for the poor and the insane. No one but Mr. Clemens could have written so movingly of what he saw there, Livy thought. What a good man he was at heart! She felt sure as he grew more interested in the church he would give up his bad habits. Livy felt both humble and proud as she thought that perhaps she had helped this man who was a genius in his work, to find his way to a better life. She was truly his sister, she told herself happily, the kind of sister she most wanted to be. Mr. Clemens would come to visit them again, soon, and he and she could talk more about these things. Meantime, she had his wonderful letters to read and re-read.

Sam made his next appearance in Elmira on a Saturday morning late in November. He had come back full of hope and plans. Livy's letters to him while he was away had told him that her feeling for him was not as sisterly as she imagined it to be, and he was determined to make her say Yes to his proposal. That evening he gave a lecture in Elmira, which the Langdons attended.

The next day was Sunday. Sam had gone home with the Langdons after the lecture and when he came downstairs the next morning, he found Livy and her parents at the breakfast table. "Will you join us at church, Mr. Clemens?" Livy asked him formally. "The services are at eleven."

Sam, startled at first, immediately recovered himself. "That was my intention," he said. "The thought of accompanying you to hear the Reverend Beecher preach was what got me out of bed so promptly this morning."

Jervis Langdon gave him a suspicious look but Livy said gently, "I'm glad, then, that I suggested it." She put her attention on her breakfast as if she were hungry, but her thoughts were elsewhere. If she wore the new bonnet bought only last week, would it look as if she were encouraging Mr. Clemens to false hopes? She decided that it would not.

In church, Livy shared a hymnbook with her guest. He sang the hymns with such enthusiasm, in his beautiful tenor, that the happiness in her heart began to grow and grow. The services were lovely and the November sun shone behind the stained glass of the windows, creating a rosy glow above the bowed heads of the congregation. Livy stole a look at her companion and then felt the color warm her face—he had caught her look and moved the hand that helped to hold the song book closer to her own, so that their fingers touched. The words on the page in front of Livy quivered and her voice stumbled over them, but after a second she recovered and ignoring Mr. Clemens' nearness, continued with the song.

Afterwards, when the two of them were sitting together in the library, Livy said, "Mr. Clemens, I don't believe you were listening to the sermon very closely."

"That is your fault then, my dear sister. You looked so bewitching in that velvet bonnet, with your little face peeping out of it, that I could not keep my mind on anything except you."

"Oh, Mr. Clemens, you mustn't—please do not say such things to me." Livy moved away from him as her father came into the room.

Dinner was announced, and then Sue and Theo came in the afternoon, and everyone went for a drive. Later, the Cranes came back to the Langdon drawing room for an evening of music and talk. Livy kept away from Sam as much as possible, although whenever he was not looking at her, her eyes strayed toward him.

All the next day, Monday, Sam followed Livy about, paying her compliments and then apologizing for doing it, saying that he could not help himself. By Monday night, when Livy reached the shelter of her bedroom, she found her emotions in turmoil. What was she to do? While Mr. Clemens had been away, she had thought of him night and day. Now that he was here again, under the very same roof, she had begun to feel that her whole life would be empty and useless unless she could become his wife as he wished her to be.

Restless, unable to sleep, Livy found her robe and slippers and stole from her room, peering over the baluster to see if there was any light burning downstairs. Mr. Clemens had gone to bed so there was no danger of running into him, and she felt that she must talk to Papa. Livy slipped down the stairs noiselessly.

She found her parents still sitting by the fire in the library. Seeing Livy, the Langdons looked alarmed.

"We thought you were asleep," her mother said. "You ought to be."

"Mama—Papa—" Livy began.

The alarm on their faces deepened and Livy hesitated. They were so kind and good, and so devoted to her.

"It's about Mr. Clemens," she said bravely. "I—I'm afraid that I love him. I cannot sleep for thinking of him. Do you really believe that it would be impossible for me to marry him?"

"Livy, my darling girl!" Jervis Langdon got to his feet and went to her. "You know it is impossible. He is a man whose life will always be one of intensity and strain. These are attributes of the creative genius that I am sure Sam Clemens is. It would never do for you to marry him, Livy. You would not be able to stand the rigors and uncertainties such a marriage would bring."

"Oh, Papa . . ." Livy turned and buried her face in her father's shoulder, weeping silently. But after a few minutes, she raised her head and said firmly, "I know you are right. Mama, you do agree with Papa, don't you?" She tried not to make the question a cry for help.

"Yes, Livy dear, I do. Mr. Clemens is not for you." Mrs. Langdon spoke tenderly, but there was no doubt in her voice.

The three of them talked for a little while about Sam Clemens and Livy's feeling for him. The Langdons asked Livy to try to avoid Sam for the rest of his visit —or at least to avoid being alone with him. She promised that she would.

All the next day Livy stuck to this promise. Whenever she saw the least chance that she would be left alone with Sam, she disappeared. And when he asked her to go walking with him, she said she had letters to write. The same thing happened in the evening. Sam was left in the parlor with Mr. and Mrs. Langdon; Livy stayed in her room.

Realizing that Livy must have discussed him with her parents, Sam brought the subject out into the open.

"I think she loves me, though not as much as I love her," he said. "I would like you, sir," he addressed Mr. Langdon, "to consider my suit without prejudice. I will guard her and protect her with all that I have for the rest of my life, if you will trust her to me."

"My dear friend," Jervis Langdon said, his affection for his visitor showing in his manner, "I wish Mrs. Langdon and I could say 'Take her with our blessing.' You know the story of her health and you know, better than we do, the story of your own life, both in the past and the one you must lead from now on. Every day, the name of Mark Twain becomes better known. How can our sheltered child undertake a life lived in the light of publicity, perhaps moving from place to place without roots? No, Clemens, much as I like you, I shall have to say No to your hopes."

Despite the firmness of this reply, Sam thought he detected some lack of conviction. He urged his suit, talking for an hour or more. When he left the Langdons to go to bed, he was whistling cheerfully under his breath. "They say NO, NO, NO," he told himself, "but I say YES, YES, YES."

The next evening, when Sam cornered Livy at last in the parlor after dinner, she admitted that she loved him. "But I am sorry that I do," she said sorrowfully. "I hope that I shall overcome this feeling you inspire in me, Mr. Clemens, since we can never, never marry. I am not strong enough and anyway, my parents cannot spare me. Sue is married and Charley is hardly ever at home. Mama and Papa have assumed that I will never leave them and I cannot, no matter what my longings are. I hope you will believe me and accept this as final."

Sam took her hand in his and kissed it on the palm. "I don't promise to do that," he said, "but I will not bother you about this again, unless your parents consent."

By the next day, Sam's persuasiveness and sincerity had worn down both Livy and her parents. They told him they would give a conditional consent to an engagement, since Livy had convinced them he was a good and noble person and would take excellent care of her.

"We cannot let it be a formal betrothal, however," Jervis Langdon said, "until we have learned more about your past. I shall have to ask you to furnish me with character references."

"I'll give you dozens!" Sam said happily. He walked to the small settee where Livy was and, holding out his hands to her, drew her to her feet. "Have you made them believe, at last, that I cannot live without you?"

"Nor I without you, Mr. Clemens," Livy said courageously.

"Sam," corrected her sweetheart.

"Samuel . . ." Livy made herself say his name, although she could not use the shortened version. Later she would tell him her special name for him, Youth.

Mrs. Langdon coughed and Sam turned Livy around to face her parents, clinging, however, to her hand.

"You will never be sorry that you have trusted me," he promised them.

Chapter Seven

Neither Sam nor Livy slept much for the next forty-eight hours. Jervis Langdon, seeing the state of excitement that Livy was in, took Sam aside and suggested that he go away for a while and give her a chance to calm down and rest. Sam, despite his reluctance to be separated from his beloved so soon, agreed. Livy looked, in Sam's own words, like a "lovely, peerless, radiant ghost" and he loved her too much to want anything except what was best for her. He said good-by, making her promise to write him often.

Livy, watching the carriage roll away down the driveway, turned to her cousin Hattie Lewis who had returned from New York in time to hear the news. "There's one thing I have made up my mind to, Hattie. If and when Mr. Clemens and I do get married, I'm not going to criticize him. He is a great man; he must be free. I couldn't bear it if he lived in dread of my criticizing him for his faults."

"Faults?" Hattie's eyebrows arched teasingly. "I thought you just told me this morning that Mr. Clemens was perfect."

Now the semi-engaged couple had to depend chiefly
on letters for the further flowering of their romance.
Sam, as Mark Twain, was delivering his popular lectures
in various parts of the country. He had to travel on slow,
creaking trains and bed down in hotel rooms, many of
them dismal. Sometimes, because of a busy schedule, he
went without sleep for as long as thirty-six hours.

But he wrote Livy at least every other day. The
letters were long and adoring, addressed now to "My
dear, dear Livy."

Livy wrote him as faithfully. Sam called her letters
eight-page "commercials" because she was so formal
and dignified in her expressions of love for him. He
chuckled, too, over the weird spellings his "funny little
orthographist" contrived. When he could, he routed
himself by way of Elmira where he could continue his
avowals in person for the girl he called "that wonderful
miracle of humanity."

Livy's father worried about the ardor of Sam's court-
ship and he bluntly asked Sam to slow it down until his
character references had been heard from. Mrs. Langdon was especially concerned about their lack of information on this man, called the wild humorist of the
sagebrush hills, who wanted to rob them of their daughter.

Livy, however, was not worried about Sam's character. She had given him her whole heart and with it
her complete trust. Writing to a motherly friend Sam
had made on board *The Quaker City*, Livy said how

proud and humble, both, it made her to have Sam's friends consider her worthy of him, especially when they said they thought she could be of help to him in his career. To help the man she loved so much by making the world understand him as she saw him, became Livy's chief wish. "He is not just a humorist," she said to her sister Sue. "He is a man with a deep, serious nature. I want everyone in the world to know it."

Livy and Sam had agreed that, despite the Langdons' wealth, they wanted to live on whatever money Sam could make. They wanted to be independent. This meant that Sam had to find something besides writing and lecturing to support them. He wanted to invest in a thriving newspaper but first he had to raise some money. While he traveled about the country on his lecture tour, he also investigated newspapers with an eye to the future.

Sam arrived in Elmira early in February, 1869, a few months after Livy had said she loved him, to find Jervis Langdon waiting for him, a pile of letters of "recommendation" on his desk. He showed some of them to Sam. One predicted that Sam Clemens "would fill a drunkard's grave."

Jervis Langdon's brows were drawn together and his jaw was stiff as he waited for Sam to look over the letters.

"Haven't you a friend in the world?" he asked.

He did have friends, Sam thought. Many of them. But if he had given Mr. Langdon their names they would have written only of his virtues, so he had given the names of other, less intimate acquaintances. Now in the face of their hostile replies, he wished he had not leaned so far backward in the matter, but it was too late. The letters were there, confronting him.

"Apparently not," he said in answer to Mr. Langdon, sighing.

There was silence in the Langdon library and Sam inwardly held his breath. Was he to lose Livy now, because of the obviously jealous hostility of a few past associates?

At last Jervis Langdon held out his hand, his features relaxing into a smile. "Then I'll be your friend myself. Take the girl. I know you better than they do."

Sam hurried off to tell Livy, wishing there were a hundred church steeples, towers, mountain peaks, in his way, so that he could leap over every one.

The formal engagement of Olivia Langdon and Samuel Clemens was set at February 4, 1869, with plans for a wedding one year from that date. Sam had to leave Elmira for about a week to fulfill his lecture engagements. When he returned on the nineteenth, he brought Livy's ring, a plain, gold band with their engagement date engraved on the inside.

To Livy, the ring seemed "the largest piece of furniture in the house," and she could scarcely keep from looking at it.

"She's afraid it will disappear," Charley teased.

During a dinner party, Hattie Lewis saw Livy manage to display her ring finger, even though it was sometimes awkward. "Is your shoulder dislocated?" she whispered.

Livy flushed and hid her hand in her lap. Let them tease. There had never been a more priceless ornament. Under the protection of the tablecloth, she stroked the metal band as if it were a magic talisman.

A year seemed long to wait, but Sam needed to be established in business. He told Livy he had paddled his own canoe since he was thirteen and would continue to. "Soon I'll find the right newspaper, and locate the money to buy a share in it. It will be a paper with a high standing; I'll work hard to make it both good and profitable. You will never have to worry about anything."

"I'll help—Samuel." Livy still stumbled over his first name, despite his teasing. "I'll cook and save and help you correct your manuscripts."

Sam smiled. The picture of his darling little protected fiancée doing any cooking was hard to believe in. But as far as his work went, Livy was already helping. The proofs of *The Innocents Abroad* had arrived. Together Sam and Livy had gone over them, and he had been amazed, amused, and gratified at the quickness with which she had spotted an awkward sentence, an improper phrase. She might be a poor speller, but she had good literary taste and high intelligence. The only thing he was concerned for was her lack of strength.

"You give too much of yourself, Livy," he said. "It worries me. Promise me that when I go off on my hateful lecture trip again, you'll sleep late. I know your father would rather do without you at breakfast than to have you tired out. I want you strong and healthy, my love." He drew her into his arms.

Livy leaned against him. "I will be," she whispered. "I'll rest and rest and rest, until you come again." She stroked his cheek, telling him for the hundredth time how deeply she loved him.

Sam let the pleasure of her caress and her loving words sink into him. He had always been reserved when it came to putting his feelings into words, except on paper. The members of his family did not kiss each other except at funerals. Livy was different, bless her. She could no more suppress her loving, affectionate nature than she could stop breathing. He was overwhelmed with the richness of emotion being offered him but unable to show his own equally strong feelings in return.

Livy, however, felt no dissatisfaction. She kept her cheek pressed against his. From his vest pocket and the folds of his coat came the sweet, musky aroma of cigar smoke. It did not seem such a sinful odor to her now, as it once had.

In spite of Sam's resolution not to rely on Livy's father for any part of their financial support after they were married, he was persuaded to let Jervis Langdon loan him money to buy an interest in the *Buffalo Express*.

"Twelve thousand five hundred dollars is a lot of money to borrow," Sam told Livy as they sat together in the Langdon library in June of the year they were engaged. The two of them had been playing cribbage —Sam loved card games and Livy was learning to enjoy them, too.

"But Papa wants you to take the loan. He thinks the *Express* is a good investment. And your new book is bound to be a success."

This was true. Elisha Bliss, Sam's Hartford publisher, said advance orders for *The Innocents Abroad* were coming in steadily. It would be out the following month. Thinking of the Blisses and other Hartford friends, Sam said, "I wish we could live in Hartford, instead of Buffalo, though."

"Wherever we live together," Livy said, "we'll be happy." The clock chimed. "Oh—I have to get dressed, Sam'l. The Hookers are expecting us."

He looked at her. She was wearing a dress of deep brown, a color she favored. "Why do you have to change, Livy? That dress is beautiful. Why haven't you let me see you in it before?"

She laughed. "Oh, Youth, Youth! You have seen it. I wore it when we went to Hartford for Alice Hooker's wedding." She had also worn it several times when Sam was at Elmira.

He laughed with her. It was not the first time, nor

the last, that he had made or would make this mistake. "It's your wearing of a gown that makes it beautiful," he said. "Anyhow, all I can remember of that day is what a gorgeous bridesmaid you were. I reckon I won't be able to stand the beauty of your being a bride."

They got up and walked from the game room hand in hand. Mrs. Langdon, catching sight of them, marveled that she could ever have had doubts about either Mr. Clemens' quality or his love. If she had any doubts now, it was of Livy. Mr. Clemens would go far. Would her daughter be equal to the demands which would be put upon her?

Chapter Eight

$\mathcal{L}$ ivy and Sam were married in the Langdon parlor in Elmira on February 2, 1870. Sam's friend from Hartford, the Reverend Joseph Twichell, and the Langdons' pastor, Thomas K. Beecher, officiated.

Watching the ceremony were Livy's close friends and relatives, Sam's sister Pamela Moffett and her daughter Annie, and Sam's mother, Jane Clemens, a tall, slim woman with clear blue eyes and a drawl like her son's.

As Livy and Sam stood in the reception line after the ceremony, Livy pressed the gold band on her finger lovingly. Her engagement ring had become her wedding ring, unchanged except for the addition of the wedding date engraved on it. Her heart was almost bursting with love and pride for the handsome man beside her. Nothing she had ever dreamed of had been as wonderful as this glorious present.

The bride and groom spent the first night of their married life under the Langdon roof, but the next morning Sam and Livy and the rest of the wedding party piled into carriages and drove to the railroad station. Jervis Langdon had arranged for a private, "palace" car for the entire group, all of them to travel with the newlyweds to their new home in Buffalo.

Sam had asked a friend of the Langdons, J. D. F. Slee, to find a boarding house that would be a suitable home for him and Livy while he was getting started with his newspaper career. As he tucked Livy into the carriage for the drive to the Elmira depot, Sam said, "I certainly hope Slee hasn't failed me. I ought to have gone to Buffalo myself and looked our future home over before taking you there."

"Dearest—" Livy began, but then made herself keep still. A big surprise was waiting for her dear Youth when they got to Buffalo—a surprise Papa had planned, telling no one except his own family. Livy was torn between delight in the surprise and fear that perhaps Samuel would not like it.

He sprang in beside her and told the driver to go. "Are you happy?" he asked her, for the tenth time that morning.

"I'm so happy I think I must have died and gone to heaven," Livy responded. Samuel would not be angry about the surprise; he couldn't be, when Papa only wanted to help them. She put her anxiety out of her mind and relaxed against her husband's shoulder. She had always loved the sound of horses' hoofs on cold, crisp roads and now it seemed the music of bliss. As the carriage struck a frozen rut, she took a firmer grasp of Sam's arm, thinking that he looked something like a bear, in his great fur coat and fur cap. An exuberant bear.

On the train, Sam's spirits rose higher and higher. He sang and joked with the members of their party, passing up and down the length of the car. Livy plucked at his sleeve once while he was singing a particularly rollicking song.

"Youth, darling—Samuel!" she cautioned.

He turned a face so shining with joy toward her that the words of remonstrance died on her lips. "I love you, love you, love you," he said, catching her hand in his.

Livy gave up. When he later pretended to take up a collection to pay his friend Joe Twichell's fee for marrying them, she laughed with the rest of the party.

It was nine in the evening when they reached Buffalo. Mr. Slee, the man who was to find them a boarding house, was waiting at the station with sleighs. Livy and Sam got into one of the sleighs, calling farewell greetings to the rest of the party, for whom Jervis Langdon had reserved rooms at a Buffalo hotel.

In the sleigh, Sam held Livy close under the horse-hair robe. "Are you cold?" he asked her.

Her laughter rang above the harness bells. Nothing could be colder than Samuel's nose against her cheek. "No, but you are, right there in the center of your face," she told him.

They rode in silent contentment for a number of

blocks, but then Sam began to fret about the slowness of
their driver. "What's the matter with the man?" he
asked Livy. "He lets the horses loaf along and besides,
I feel certain we have gone down this very street once
before. Do you suppose he doesn't know the way?"

"Of course he does," Livy assured him. She knew the
driver had been given orders to take as long as possible
to reach his destination. It was part of the surprise. "Do
keep calm, Samuel." She clasped his hand more tightly.
"Dear heart—dear husband," she murmured. She could
go on riding forever behind the horses, she thought, as
long as he was there beside her.

Sam was quiet again for a while but then a sign saying "Delaware Street" flashed into view. He sat up
straight. "What are we doing in this part of town? Slee
must think I'm a millionaire, to want to live in a boarding house on Delaware Street."

Before his concern could become a blast of temper,
the sleigh stopped in front of a mansion whose windows
blazed with light. "There's some mistake, Livy," Sam
said, frowning. "We'll have to see what's happened."
He got out and helped her down. Together they walked
up to the entrance of the handsome house, Livy not
knowing whether to laugh or cry. Poor, beloved Youth.
He was staring at the expensive house as if it repre-
sented financial ruin. "We can never stay here, Livy,"
he said.

"Let's go inside anyway, as long as we're here," she
said. "There will be a fire and we can get warm."

They walked past some elm trees and under a decorated entrance arch. The door was opened and as they stepped inside, a servant came to take their wraps. Odors of roasting meat blended with that of wood smoke from a crackling fire. Sparkling chandeliers cast reflected light on polished wood and blue satin gleamed at the windows and on the upholstered furniture. Even to Livy, who had chosen the furnishings, the place seemed a fairyland.

Sam simply stared. Livy put a hand on his arm. "It's ours, Youth dear. All of it, everything—a gift from Papa."

"What? What did you say?" Sam stood there, dazed.

Jervis Langdon stepped up then and handed Sam a box. "Here's the deed, proof that it is your property," he said.

With everyone watching him, Sam opened the box. He lifted out the papers and looked at them, scarcely knowing what he read. Then he looked up, his mouth working and tears in his eyes. "Well," he said, "well —I just want to say, Mr. Langdon, whenever you are in Buffalo, if it's twice a year, come right here. Bring your bag and stay overnight, if you want to. It shan't cost you a cent."

There was appreciative laughter but Livy saw tears in the eyes of several of the guests.

It was midnight before all the guests had gone. Together Sam and Livy went from room to room, examining and exclaiming. Ellen, the cook, appeared to ask what Livy would like to order for the morning's marketing.

Livy looked helplessly at Sam. She had never given market orders in her life. "Is there anything special you'd like, Samuel?" she asked.

He thought a minute. "Well, I suppose we could order some beefsteak." He asked Ellen, "Does it come by the yard or the barrel?"

Ellen, smiling at their inexperience, said she would do the ordering herself, then.

One other servant, a brisk young Irishman, came to introduce himself, before Livy and Sam could go to bed.

"I'm Patrick McAleer," he said.

"Good morning to ye, then, Patrick," Sam said, his mouth twitching into a smile. "Because it is morning now, you know. I take it you are the coachman?"

Patrick smiled, a smile that won Sam's and Livy's hearts at once. "That's right, sir. Just let Ellen know or send someone to the stables, when you need me. I'll be ready and waiting and so will the horses."

They thanked him and told him goodnight.

"And now, Mrs. Clemens," Sam said to Livy, "your husband is going to carry you upstairs and tuck you into bed. Tomorrow is the beginning of a new life."

When Sam and Livy had been married a week, Sam wrote a report to the Langdons on Livy's progress as a homemaker, grinning to himself as he did so. Everything was going smoothly, he said, although "she has a dreadful time economizing a turkey in such a way as to make him last a week." The servants, he wrote, were required to set down all purchases in an account book "to be critically scanned by her eagle eye." Puffing on a cigar—he was trying to limit himself to smoking only between three and five o'clock—he added, "The plain fact of the matter is that she has undergone the most astounding change—for verily she has become so boisterous, so noisy, & so lawless in her cheery happiness that I, even I, am forced to put on an irksome gravity & decorum in order to uphold the dignity of the house. She pulls & hauls me around, & claws my hair, & bites my fingers . . . it does appear to me that I never saw anybody so happy as she is in all my life—except myself."

Livy added a postscript, saying, "We are happy as two mortals well can be."

The two co-authored many letters to their friends and families, taking turns watching over each other's shoulders. When Sam wrote to a friend, "There is no romance in this existence for Livy," she seized the pen and wrote, "False."

"We have been married eleven days," he wrote in the same letter, "and not thirty-five cross words have passed between us." Again Livy claimed the pen. "Not one," she inserted.

Her first letter as a bride had gone to her family. "I wish that I could remember some of the funny things that Mr. Clemens says and does, and besides these funny things, he is so tender and considerate in every way."

In a letter of his own to an old friend from his Nevada mining days, Sam wrote, after a month of marriage: "If all of one's married days are as happy as these new ones have been to me, I have deliberately fooled away 30 years of my life. If I were to do over again I would marry in early infancy instead of wasting time cutting teeth and breaking crockery."

To both Livy and Sam, their marriage seemed so exciting that it was hard to think of the outside world. They felt "burdened and bent" with happiness those first months in Buffalo, even though Sam was bored with his work on the *Buffalo Express* and Livy had some trouble learning to manage a household.

Then, in June of the year they were married, a telegram from Elmira told them that Jervis Langdon was very ill. They went home at once, remaining in Elmira until Mr. Langdon's death on August 7. It was a difficult, sorrowful summer for Livy and Sam. The death of Livy's father deprived Sam of one of the best friends he had ever had, and Livy lost the man she loved better than any in the world, except her husband.

"I wish he could have lived to see his grandchild," Livy said sadly to Sam, when it was all over. "Papa would have been so happy for us."

For answer, Sam could only hold her in his arms and comfort her with his strength and his love.

Chapter Nine

*L*ivy Clemens inherited a quarter of a million dollars from her father, as her share of the Langdon wealth. Sam and Livy sat in the living room of their house in Buffalo, after their return home from Elmira, and discussed their financial affairs. Things were going well for Sam. *The Innocents Abroad* was bringing in twelve hundred dollars or more a month. The manuscript on which he was working, *Roughing It,* about his gold mining and frontier newspaper days, should do as well, he felt.

"We won't touch a penny of your inheritance for living expenses," he said to Livy. "If you want to buy some little treasures for the house or yourself, then I suppose you can use some of it," he added with a smile. Livy looked up from her task of sewing fine lace on an infant petticoat for the expected baby and returned his smile. "Would it be all right if I sometimes bought a treasure for you, too, sir?" she asked.

Sam nodded. He was thinking that after the baby came, he would try to sell his share in the *Buffalo Express.* Writing and lecturing, not newspaper work, were what would provide the riches for Livy that he wanted her to have. She had overtired herself these past months, first by helping to nurse her father, and then afterward by nursing a friend, Emma Nye, who had come to stay with Livy while Sam was away from home, and had contracted typhoid fever, dying in Livy's bedroom. August and September had been anxious months for Sam. He did not like to see Livy so pale and tired.

In October, however, the shadows lifted. Livy's brother Charley married his long-time sweetheart, Ida Clark, an event which pleased everyone. And on November 7, a few weeks earlier than he was expected, a boy was born to Sam and Livy Clemens.

Livy looked at the frail infant with love and pride mixed with anxiety. "He's terribly thin," she said to Sam.

Sam, sitting beside her bed, smoothed her high, white forehead and studied his son. "Don't worry. I was premature, too. I didn't amount to much until I was six years old. You wait, in a few months he'll be able to lick his weight in wild cats."

"Or tame cats?" Livy asked mischievously. Sam was very fond of cats and there were always one or more around, either in the house or being fed at the door.

They named the baby Langdon, in memory of Livy's father. In spite of Sam's hopeful prediction, he did not grow very fast. Neither did Livy grow stronger. Watching the snow descend from a gray Buffalo sky, she yearned for home.

"When spring comes," Sam promised, "we'll go back to Elmira. Then, after I sell my interest in the *Express*, we'll move to Hartford."

Spring came, finally, and they left for Elmira to spend the summer at Quarry Farm.

On the long hill overlooking the Chemung River, Livy slowly recovered her strength. By day she could see trees and grass and watch the birds raising their families. At night, if she could not sleep, the twinkling, familiar lights of Elmira were friendly beacons.

Sam, meanwhile, pegged away at the new book, *Roughing It*, although he had lost his earlier optimism about it.

"It will have no success," he told Livy.

"Oh, Youth," she protested, "you're giving in to gloom. As soon as I'm able to, I will read it with you—"

He smiled. "I've put in swear words just for you to have the pleasure of taking them out."

"You know, darling, that the swear words are not my basic concern. I want you to do the very finest writing you can, so that the world will know you are the best."

He lifted her hands and kissed them. "I know, Livy. If I'm gloomy at times it's because I can't stand to see you so weak and pale."

"Langdon has a cough again," Livy said, "and I worry."

"He'll be all right," Sam assured her. "It's the colic again, the doctor says. When Langdon gets his teeth, he's going to bite that doctor good, for all those medicines he keeps forcing down his little throat."

"I do love him so," Livy said.

"The doctor?" Sam looked indignant.

"You. So much more than I can ever say," Livy answered.

The door opened and the nurse brought in the baby.

Livy raised her arms hungrily. She held the infant in the curve of her arm, one hand tenderly touching the tiny nose, the pale cheek, the alabaster forehead.

"I think he's gaining weight, don't you, Sam'l?" she asked.

He nodded, pride and hope in his eyes, too.

By late April, Livy could walk three or four steps holding onto a chair. And every other day, she was able to ride a few blocks. Although Livy could not hear the scratch of pens from her bedroom, she knew that Samuel's new book was going swiftly on its way again. She and Sam had decided to make their home in Hartford, Connecticut, as soon as she was strong enough. This time, Livy thought, she would know more about managing a home than she had when she arrived in Buffalo.

Livy and Sam and little Langdon moved to Hartford in October, renting one of several homes in a settlement known as Nook Farm. Sam, his interest in the *Buffalo Express* sold, set out on a lecture tour as soon as he felt that Livy was established in their new home. The fact that she would be surrounded with good neighbors and friends made leaving her somewhat easier, much as he dreaded returning to his old, wearisome lecture life. But they needed more money than his writing would bring in.

Once again, Sam and Livy wrote out their love in letters. Livy, listening for the postman in the soft whiteness of December snow, could scarcely believe that the two of them had been separated for two months and would be for two more. It was only half living, to have Sam away from her for so long a time.

The lecture tour ended in early February and was a great success. *Roughing It*, published the same month, was also successful. Sam, at home at last, told Livy, "The advance sale is so good that I'll never have to lecture or sit at an editor's desk for the rest of my days. From now on, I'll only write books."

"That's what I was hoping for! Oh, Sam'l! To think you will never have to be separated from me and the baby for any long period again." She put her arms around his neck and kissed him on the cheek. "I cannot spare you, I truly cannot."

In March, the Clemenses set off for Elmira so Livy could have her second child at Quarry Farm.

The new baby, a golden-haired girl, was born March 19. They named her Olivia Susan Clemens, but she was called Susy.

This time, Livy recovered faster than anyone had hoped. She was soon able to go for rides in the carriage, take short walks, and supervise with loving care the handling of her two children.

"I haven't time to be sick or lie abed," she told her friend Clara Spaulding when Clara expressed amazement at Livy's sprightliness. "Sam and I are planning our dream house—we worked on it evenings last year, too, whenever he was home. And oh, Clara, Sam says we are to make a trip to Europe, before long. I can scarcely believe it. To think of me, Livy Langdon, being the mother of two adorable children and planning a trip abroad!"

"How is the German coming?" Clara asked her. Livy had written from Hartford that her washwoman, a German, was helping her to study that language.

"It's terrible. All those strange verb endings— I sometimes think I shall never manage it."

"I think you will. You have a very strong will, Livy. It's what holds you up whenever everyone expects you to fall down," Clara laughed.

By late May, Sam and Livy, after a brief trip to Cleveland with Sam's mother, were back in Hartford with their two children.

"This is the only place, except Elmira, which will ever seem home to me," Livy said one evening to Sam. They were taking turns reading aloud to one another, but she interrupted to express her contentment.

Sam yawned sleepily. "Let's ask Charles and Lily Warner for dinner tomorrow night. Charles ought to be back from New York early in the day." Charles Dudley Warner was a writer who lived next door to the Clemens' household; Lily was his wife. The four young married people were close friends and met almost daily.

Livy smiled at Sam. "I have already spoken to Lily. I knew you would want to see them as soon as he came home."

Sam shook his head, staring at her. "Watch that mind-reading, Mrs. Clemens. One of these days you might find some of those words you dislike so much, lying right there on the surface of my brain."

Livy's smile grew until it was almost a laugh. "There is no need to read your mind for those," she said. "I was in the hall this morning when you lost your pencil. I only hope no one else was." But she rose and going to him, laid her cheek against his warm hand to take away the scolding note of her words.

Again, however, Sam and Livy's happiness received a blow. In May, little Langdon's cough grew worse. "It's only croup again," Sam said without conviction.

But Livy shook her head. This was something much worse than croup.

The doctor called it diphtheria and on June 2, 1872, Langdon Clemens died.

Sam blamed himself for the child's death, because he had taken Langdon out for an airing and had let the furs covering the child's legs slip down. Livy tried to comfort him and herself at the same time; there was the new baby, dear little Susy, to consider.

Chapter Ten

Although Sam and Livy had dreamed of a trip to Europe together, in August of that year, 1872, Sam had to go to England alone. Publishers there were planning to sell his book without giving him any payment. Livy was not pleased to be separated from him again so soon, but she knew it was necessary for him to go.

"I hope to do a book on England and the English," he told her. "And give lectures. If those English people like me, I will make enough money to justify a trip later and take you and Susy with me."

Livy's mother came to stay with her and the baby while Sam was gone. She was there when Livy received a letter from Sam describing his voyage.

"Just listen to this, Mama," Livy said, smiling and shaking her head as she scanned the familiar handwriting. "Sam'l says that he stood high on the stern of the ship, looking this way, and yelling '*I love you, Livy darling!*'"

Mrs. Langdon, who was holding Susy in her lap and stroking the soft yellow down on her head, said, "If he really did such a thing, everyone must have stared. Of course, I'm sure it is just something he made up."

"It is not," Livy declared. Although Sam was not above making up stories to please her, it would be like him to do just what he said he had done. Anyway, she preferred to think that he had. Grief over little Langdon's death lingered and she also still missed her father very much. It helped her spirits to think that Sam was reasonably cheerful, for he, too, must be mourning in his heart.

Sam returned from England in November, full of plans. They were all to go abroad the next summer, he said. And he was going to build one of the most comfortable and beautiful homes in Connecticut for Livy.

The winter was a happy one. Susy was thriving. Evenings were festive, with dinner parties at their own home or at those of their many interesting and intellectual neighbors.

The Charles Dudley Warners were, perhaps, their most frequent guests. One evening, Charles and Sam started discussing how stupid and inept most current novels were.

"Why don't you two write a better one, then?" Livy challenged them.

Lily Warner backed her up. "Yes. It's easy to criticize but not so easy to perform."

As a result, the two men began to collaborate on a novel, to be called *The Gilded Age.*

Livy and Susy went for a brief visit to Elmira in

April. They were to go abroad in May, taking Clara Spaulding with them; Livy wanted to see her mother and Sue and Theo before she went.

Sam, busy with Charles Warner on the novel, wrote from Hartford that the book was going well and that although he was lonesome for Livy, the family cat and her kittens were a comfort.

Livy said to Sue Crane, when she read the letter, "Sometimes, I think if Sam'l had to choose between me and the cats, he would choose the cats." But she knew better.

They sailed for England in May as planned and Sam's lectures there were all that he had hoped for. He was, in fact, so lionized by the Londoners that he and Livy decided to run away to Edinburgh, Scotland, for a time.

Despite the vacation in Edinburgh, Livy was unable to enter into the London social life that followed Sam's successes with any enthusiasm. It was the first time in her life that she had been thousands of miles from home, and she felt the separation from family and friends very keenly. So, in the fall, Sam escorted her and Clara Spaulding and Susy back home and returned to England alone to complete his engagements there.

Livy, waiting at home in Hartford for her husband's return, sometimes wondered if it would have been wiser to have let Sam accept some of the American lecture offers which had been made him. He had turned down as much as eight hundred dollars a night, because they had both hoped at the time that he would never have to lecture again. But they needed money. The house they were planning would cost a great deal, and Sam still insisted that she must not spend her inheritance on it. Most of her father's money ought to be passed on to Livy's children, he felt. To some extent, Livy agreed. And yet, she yearned for a home of her own in which to bring up her children in comfort and security, the kind of home that her parents had provided for her and Sue and Charley. Another child was on the way; it was time to think of striking roots.

Folding Sam's latest letter, she put it in the box which held all the others she had received from him, and went into the nursery.

"Your father is still not sure when he can come home," she told Susy. "He sends you his love, and told me to kiss you fifteen times for him."

Susy, who had just wakened from her nap, stood up in her crib and said something that sounded amazingly like "Ach, himmel!"

More likely, Livy thought, cuddling the golden head to her, Susy had said, "Ach, Samuel!"

The new baby was born June 8 at Quarry Farm. Sam had finally come home in January, and in April the entire family went to the farm to stay until the baby was born.

"Now, Livy," Sam said when he had looked over his

newest daughter, "I do think you are being unjust. First, Susy is born with eyes like yours and now you expect me to keep silent when you give me a second one having your lovely dark hair. When is the Clemens side of the family to have its chance?"

"I am so sorry," Livy said demurely. "Perhaps they will both *be* like you, even if they do not look so."

"Heaven forbid!" Sam exclaimed. He kissed her and told her to rest, that he was going out to the studio Sue Crane had had built for him. "I will sit and think how to teach my daughters to respect their father," he said and left her.

The studio to which Sam referred was on a knoll which overlooked most of the Chemung Valley and gave Sam a view of the distant blue hills. Octagonal, it had a peaked roof and eight windows. The Crane's gardener had trained ivy over its walls and it stood in the midst of morning glories and other flowers. In spite of its airiness, it was soon permeated with tobacco—a sign that Sam was working.

They called the second daughter Clara but she was soon nicknamed "Bay" by Susy who could not say "Baby."

That summer was a golden one for the Clemens family. The children were well, Livy seemed stronger than she had ever been, and Sam was progressing with the book about his own childhood which had been haunting him—*Tom Sawyer*. Livy, holding baby Clara in her arms or taking Susy along the paths leading to the duck pond, glanced toward Sam's study from time to time. She had seen only a few pages of the manuscript as yet but she felt sure it would be the best he had ever done. She smiled to herself as she thought this—her sister told her that she always said Sam's newest work would be his best.

Sam and Livy's dream house, at 351 Farmington Avenue in Hartford, was ready for occupancy by October. Built of brick painted with ornate designs, the house stood on spacious grounds that included a small river and woods. It rose three stories to a sloping roof and a maze of turrets, balconies and small chimneys. On one side and on the rear was a large porch. A semi-circular conservatory, with a fountain, was off the library. On the top floor was a billiard room. Unlike most houses of its time, the kitchen and the servants' quarters were in front—in order, Sam said, that the servants would not have to run to the front yard to watch parades go by.

The house was elegantly furnished and included a carved wooden mantelpiece with a brass plate on which was inscribed "The ornament of a house is the friends that frequent it."

Beyond the house stood huge stables and carriage sheds. Exclusive of the furniture, the place cost $135,-000—a rich man's home.

For Mark Twain was growing rich. All that was necessary, Livy thought as she wandered happily through the still not quite settled rooms of her new home, was that Samuel continue to write, writing his very best.

Chapter Eleven

*T*he Hartford house was everything that Sam and
Livy had hoped for, although some adjustments had to
be made for Sam's creative problems. He found himself
unable to work in his study and turned it over to the
children for a playroom. The billiard room, at the top
of the house, became his working place; whenever the
work would not go, he stopped for a game and to think.

Sam Clemens' children early discovered his gift for
telling stories, and the library in Hartford became the
favorite place for this activity. On the shelves and the
mantel of the fireplace were a variety of decorative
objects. A framed oil painting of a cat's head, a life-
size watercolor of the head of a young girl known as
Emmeline, a picture called "The Young Medusa," and
a dozen or more other art objects were in the library.

"Tell us about Emmeline, Papa!" Susy or Bay would
say when they found their father in the library. Sam
would then be expected to bring to life all the ornaments
and paintings in a story.

To Livy he complained, "Those poor bits of bric-a-
brac of yours ought to have a day of rest. I've kept them

busy jumping off bridges or shooting Indians every day
for so long it's making me feel a sinner." Both of the
children were on his lap at the moment. So were two
cats.

Livy, listening to the storytelling, merely smiled. She
knew that Sam loved the story hours as much as the
children did, and almost as much as she did.

"If you want a rest," she said, "I will read to them."

"No, Mama!" three-year-old Bay said peremptorily.
"Papa said he would tell about a bawgun strictor. I want
to hear about the bawgun strictor."

"She means a boa constrictor," Susy explained to her
mother. Susy considered herself very grown-up compared to Clara.

Sam and Livy exchanged smiles, and Sam plunged
into a long tale of a snake which wrapped itself around
poor Emmeline's neck, but due to the magic charm of
one of the other articles on the mantel, Emmeline was
able to free herself and kill the snake.

It was the winter of 1877. Sam and Livy had lived
in the Hartford house over three years, years filled with
comfort and happiness. Surrounded by the friends they
enjoyed most and with money enough to entertain
lavishly, Livy felt she had achieved the life she had
dreamed of for herself and her loved ones.

A mother with very high standards of behavior, Livy
was also a just and loving one. Susy was a shy, dreamy,
emotionally intense child, with a keen sense of dignity.

One day when Lily Warner was calling on Livy, Susy kept interrupting their conversation.

Finally, Livy said, with unusual sharpness, "Susy, if you interrupt again, I will send you to the nursery."

Mrs. Warner went home a few minutes later. As Livy returned from the front door, she saw Susy making her way upstairs, her face solemn.

"Where are you going, Susy?"

"To the nursery."

"What are you going up there for, dear?" Livy asked, having forgotten her own threat. "Don't you want to stay with me in the library?"

Susy, eyes grave under her curls, shook her head. "You didn't speak to me right, Mama."

Puzzled, Livy asked, "What do you mean?"

"You didn't speak to me *right*, Mama," Susy repeated, and then explained that it had not been proper for Livy to scold her in front of someone.

Livy picked up Susy and carried her to the library, trying to impress on her that she had to be spoken to sharply at times, if she were to learn how to behave. At the end of Livy's lecture, Susy repeated, unmoved, "But you didn't speak to me *right*."

Amused and remorseful at the same time, Livy knew when she was beaten. "I'm sorry I hurt your feelings. Perhaps I didn't speak to you right," she admitted.

Susy was always so sensitive that Livy felt apprehension for her, but Clara was different. Brunette, in con-

trast to Susy's blondness, she was also bolder and more
practical. To shut Susy into a closet as punishment was
almost more than Livy could do. Clara, however, was
another matter. Livy left her second daughter in the
closet one day for about fifteen minutes. When she
went to open the door again, she heard a humming
sound. Clara was playing happily in an imaginary cave.
The clothes hanging from the hooks in the closet had
become friendly fairies. She looked contentedly up at
her mother and asked if she could play there the rest of
the day.

Once, while Clara was still quite small, she developed
a painful boil on her hand. Livy screwed up her courage
to lance the boil while Susy stood by, trembling, to
watch. Clara, though she winced, did not cry.

"Isn't she brave, Mama?" Susy asked.

Livy patted Clara's cheek. "Well, you *are* a brave
little thing," she said.

Clara responded proudly, "There's nobody braver
but God!"

They were good children, or at least their father
thought so. He dedicated his book *The Prince and the
Pauper:* "To those good-mannered and agreeable children, Susy and Clara Clemens."

They were not always good, however. Both of them
were high-strung and Susy had a passionate temper
which often expressed itself in giving Clara a whack.
When spankings failed, Livy tried bribery. For a while
she paid Clara three cents a day not to quarrel with Susy.

Susy became sick and Clara was shut out of her sister's room for two days. To Livy's amused surprise, Clara informed her that she was behind two days in her payment for Clara's good behavior.

"But you haven't seen Susy for two days, so how could you quarrel with her?" Livy asked.

"Why, Mama, don't you count that?" asked the indignant Clara.

In 1878, unable to sustain his interest in a new book with a background similar to that of *The Adventures of Tom Sawyer*, Sam Clemens decided to take his family to Europe. Taking Clara Spaulding with them, Sam, Livy, Susy, and Clara sailed on April 11 on a ship called the *Holsatia*. Clara was four years old and Susy six. Although the children's father found the *Holsatia* exceedingly noisy and complained of the shrieking of children, the clatter of an old piano, and the pounding of the ship's screw, Susy and Clara loved the ship. They were taken all over it, making friends with passengers and crew.

Livy and her friend Clara Spaulding and the two children took quarters in Hamburg, Germany, while Sam and his long-time Hartford friend Joe Twichell went on a walking tour through Germany and Switzerland—a tour which later formed the basis for a book, *A Tramp Abroad*.

The Clemens children were given school lessons at a very early age, including foreign languages. Livy taught

them herself until they were about four, and then
governesses took over. When they settled in Germany,
Livy found private teachers for the girls, young though
they were, so they could continue with their studies. She
and Clara Spaulding were still studying the German
language. Sam said German ought to be set aside among
the dead languages because only the dead had time to
learn it, but the Clemens family often conversed in a
mixture of German and English in later years.

All of the children's education in Europe did not
come from books. Livy and Sam, when he returned
from his tour, took the little girls with them when they
visited historic places and art galleries. They went to
Venice and floated in gondolas, the children picking up
Italian phrases from the gondoliers.

One of Livy's chief pleasures was to prowl through
shops in search of unusual or beautiful articles of furniture. She took Sam and the children with her when she
could and in one antique store they came upon a remarkable bed.

"Look, Sam'l," Livy said, pointing to the fat, wooden
cherubs that decorated each of the four posts of the bed.

The Italian owner of the store said something in
broken English, and when they did not understand him,
he unscrewed one of the dolls from its post, holding it
out to Susy with a smile.

"Me, too!" Bay held out her hands.

So the man unscrewed a second cherub for Clara.

"Buy it, Mama, please buy it," Susy begged.

Livy looked at Sam, who said, "You're the queen in these matters, Livy. Do as you please."

They bought the bed and had it sent home to Hartford. It was installed in Livy's room and whenever the children were sick, they were put to bed in it and allowed to play with the cherub-dolls.

The Clemenses stayed in Munich that winter and early in 1879 went to Paris, where they stayed until July. From there they went to Belgium and Holland and then to England, sailing for home on August 23, 1879.

The Hartford house, which had been closed for the year and a half they were away, was opened up and the servants, most of whom had been with them since their marriage, got it ready for the family. Livy was the kind of mistress who made friends of those who served her —if she did not like them well enough to make them her friends, she did not keep them. Patrick McAleer, the Irish coachman Livy's father had hired for them in Buffalo, had come with them to Hartford. He was married the year after Sam and Livy and brought his wife to live in a house that the Clemenses built for him next to his stable.

Sam said Patrick was a genius. "I never tell him what to do," he told a friend. "The horses are cared for and have shoes when they need them. The carriages and sleighs are kept in perfect order and all this without consulting me. A good thing, too"—the blue-green eyes gleamed under the thick eyebrows as Sam spoke—"because I'm no good at giving orders."

Another servant of the Clemenses was George Griffin, the Negro butler. He had come one day to wash windows and Livy had liked him so well that she hired him. George stayed with them eighteen years, Patrick McAleer, for thirty-six years.

George Griffin's presence in the Clemens household caused concern to one of their younger guests, John Howells, son of Mark Twain's good friend William Dean Howells, editor of *The Atlantic Monthly*. The Howells, like the Langdons and Clemenses, had been very much on the side of the North during the Civil War. When the dark-skinned George was seen by John Howells to be serving meals and doing other household chores, he complained to his parents that the Clemenses were keeping a Negro slave.

The Clemens children had almost everything they could wish for. Clara was very young when she received a huge music box of brown polished wood. It played such tunes as "The Pilgrim's Chorus" from *Tannhauser* and the "Lohengrin Wedding March." Both Clara and Susy were taught piano at a very early age, first by Livy and later by Lily Warner, who was the most accomplished amateur pianist in Hartford. When the girls' father was away, he sent them gifts of dolls and toys to compensate for his absence. When he was home, he hauled them on sleds through the snow in winter or took them for drives in summer. Sometimes he even pulled Livy on a sled, after a fresh snowfall, to call on their neighbors. On one occasion, when Clara was recovering from an accident to her leg, her father ordered one hundred valentines sent to her on Valentine's Day. She was only six when she was given a piano for Christmas.

Christmas was a big event in the Clemens household. Livy wanted no one forgotten, from Sam's famous friends to the garbage man. Using Sam's billiard room and another room as headquarters, she packed dozens of baskets with turkey, canned goods, candy, nuts, raisins, and wearing apparel.

On Christmas Eve, the Clemens children hung up their stockings in the schoolroom which was next to the nursery. Sam and Livy came into their daughters' rooms after the little girls had been put to bed by the nurse, and Livy recited " 'Twas the Night Before Christmas" for them. Sam put on a Santa Claus suit and pranced around the room, pretending he had to get warm after the long, cold drive from the North Pole. When he was warm enough, he sat down and told the half-believing little girls about his adventures on the trip down to earth.

"Now if I happened to make some mistakes in your presents," he said when he had finished his stories, "you can blame it on my servants." He pulled at his long white beard thoughtfully and then added, "Perhaps you

would like to thank me now, for whatever you will receive tomorrow. If I wait until you see your gifts, I
might not get thanked at all."

Squealing and giggling, the girls thanked Santa Claus
for what they hoped they would find in their stockings
the next morning.

On Christmas morning, if there was enough snow,
Sam and the children went out in the sleigh, with
Patrick to drive the horses, and delivered the gifts Livy
had got ready. Dressed in his big fur coat, Sam handed
the packages to the children and told them to call out
the names of the recipients. Livy felt that through this
immediate experience of gift-giving, the children learned
the true meaning of Christmas.

The long winter evenings after Christmas were never
long for Clara and Susy Clemens. If their father was
home, he told them stories. If he was not, or was too
busy, their mother read to them from *At the Back of
the North Wind* or *The Days of Bruce* or *Robinson
Crusoe*. Whatever the story, the Clemens parlor was a
warm and happy place, despite the howling of the
winter wind beyond the walls of the house. The fireplace crackled a pleasant accompaniment to the soft
purring of whatever cats were in residence. Later, after
the little girls went to bed, neighbors might drop in,
but Livy put family life before any other.

Chapter Twelve

*E*very summer that they were not abroad, Sam and Livy took their children to Elmira to spend the long, warm days at the Cranes' Quarry Farm.

In the summer of 1880, following their year and a half in Europe, Jean Clemens, like her sisters, was born at Quarry Farm. Following her birth, two new servants joined the Clemenses' staff. One was Katy Leary, a stalwart, black-eyed, black-haired Irish girl of seventeen, a native of Elmira, who was to remain with the Clemenses for the rest of Livy's life. The other was a German nurse who spoke so little English that Jean learned German with her English and for years spoke in a mixture of the two languages.

All of the Clemenses were fond of animals but it was Jean's strongest trait. At Quarry Farm, this had a good chance to develop—the children fed the ducks and chickens and visited the other animals daily.

Sam could not be with the family all of the time, having business to attend to in Hartford and New York. When he was at the farm, however, he spent much time with his children, especially out of doors.

Jean was about four years old when she developed a passion for cows. She was too young to be allowed in the barn alone so someone had to take her, at about six o'clock every evening, to watch the milking of the cows. There were three of these animals—Blanche, Jean, and "the cross cow." When Sam was available, he took Jean to see the cows.

"I wouldn't mind so much if the little bunny would carry on a conversation with me," Sam said to Livy. "She's an entertaining conversationalist. But in the barn she just sits, looking as though Christmas had come. If she says anything, it's about the cows or to them, not to me."

Livy, who was on the veranda listening to Susy read a story in Latin, said, with a flash of humor, "Be patient, Sam'l, and perhaps one of these evenings the cows will answer her. Think what a triumph that would be!"

Susy, whose brows had been bent with the struggle to translate her story, looked up then and laughed. It was a very funny idea for Mama to have—it was usually Papa who said things like that.

Sam, getting no sympathy, went to find Jean and take her to the barn.

After the milking, the hired man let the cows out to a cow lot and Jean insisted on watching them for another half-hour. Sam, looking at the mud and manure in which the cows stood, found this part of the excursion even worse than the session in the barn. When the half-hour was up, he said, "Come along, Jeanie, let's get back to Mama."

Jean gave a great sigh, took a last look at her beloved animals, and said, "Ain't this a sweet little garden?"

While Jean was still quite young, she formed a humane society in Elmira. Clara became a member and in later years, when the girls traveled abroad with their parents, they carried their blue membership cards with them proudly. As an adolescent, Jean joined the humane society of every town in which she lived, including Vienna and a town in Switzerland.

One summer, when the Clemenses arrived at Quarry Farm, they found a new and fascinating creature waiting. The Cranes had bought a donkey in Kansas and had it shipped to the farm.

Livy, expecting Jean to be the first to rush to the donkey, was surprised when the little girl went shyly and cautiously toward the animal, murmuring "Dear old fellow," unaware that the donkey was female.

The donkey was named Kaditchin. The children were allowed to catch her in the field—if they could—and put a bridle on her. The older girls were permitted to mount her.

"But no one is to go for a ride unless Papa is with you," Livy ruled. "The donkey might run away with you."

Far from running off with anyone, Kaditchin could not be made to move unless one of the children walked ahead of her with a box of crackers held just out of reach. On hot days there was a lot of argument about who was to sit on Kaditchin's back and who was to walk ahead with the crackers.

One warm day Sam was sitting on the porch listening to these arguments. He got up and came down the steps.

"I'll make her go," he said, his jaw set. "Even a donkey has to earn her feed in this world."

He hauled himself onto the donkey's back, giving the beast a kick with his heels. Kaditchin moved one of her long ears, lowered her head, and raised her hind legs. The famous Mark Twain went sailing through the air to land on his back in the grass.

All three of the girls laughed, and every time they looked at their father all the rest of the day, they giggled over the incident. Sam enjoyed the joke as much as the girls did. He claimed that he had never been as fond of Kaditchin as he was after that.

"That donkey's like you, Livy," he told her later that day. "She's graceful and serene, even when she's out for revenge." They were at dinner except for Jean, who was still young enough to have most of her meals in the nursery. As often happened, Sam paced up and down the room between courses, talking as he walked. He came back to the table and sat down. "I admire that donkey," he said. "I declare I do."

"You can't mean that I am revengeful," Livy charged him, mildly hurt that Sam compared her to the donkey.

"I would like you to name me one single instance where I have sought revenge."

He put his hand on her shoulder and looked down into her face. "You, Livy?" he asked, and now there was no humor in his face, only a gentle wonderment. "You couldn't bear a grudge if you tried. I was only fooling, like the fool that I am."

Livy blushed. She had not meant to draw so much attention to herself—but she was deeply touched by this testimonial from the man she loved so much, in front of their children and her sister and brother-in-law. To change the subject, she said, "At least you proved that the donkey is not always patient, Sam'l."

Quarry Farm was the scene of many birthday celebrations. Clara's birthday, which was June 8, sometimes occurred before the Clemenses reached the farm in summer, but Jean's, on July 26, was nearly always while they were there. When Jean was five, her father had to be away on her birthday, but he did not forget it. He wired her sixty-five returns of the day.

This was the summer of 1885. Livy began to teach Jean to read right after her birthday. Every morning the little girl would announce that she did not think she wanted a German lesson that day, but every day Livy, fond but conscientious, said, "Oh yes, darling, we must have our lesson." She took Jean into the parlor of the farmhouse, sat on the sofa by the bay window, and began the lesson. Once it was started, Jean sometimes asked for it to continue past the usual half-hour.

Livy tried to teach her children as much as possible about nature and the world around them. They read books on the natural sciences together and studied the animals, insects, and birds they saw. That same summer, Livy began to show Jean something about insects.

"We'll go outdoors and find a grasshopper," she told the little girl, taking her by the hand. "A dead one, if we can." Livy believed that killing things unnecessarily, even insects, was harmful to a child's mind. They did not find a dead grasshopper but managed to capture one alive, but it was so lively that Jean could not see how it was made.

"We'll try some other bug, Jean, one that doesn't jump about quite so much."

They let the grasshopper go and found a ladybug. It was quieter so Jean was able to examine it a little more in detail. Later, after supper, Livy caught some moths that came too near the flame of the oil lamp, and showed Jean the various parts of the moth's anatomy.

"I have a dead fly in my room, Mama," Jean said. "Shall I go and get it?"

Livy hugged her youngest daughter to her, pleased at the keenness of the child's interest. "Tomorrow we will find all the dead insects we can, darling, and look at them together."

The children had their supper earlier than Sam and Livy and Sue and Theo that next evening, and were outdoors for an hour of play while the adults were eating.

Livy had taken only a few bites of her dinner when Jean came running into the dining room and, rushing to her mother's place, laid a handful of dead flies down on the table. "I found them all in the kitchen!" she cried happily.

Sam looked across the table at Livy. "Pleasant eating, Mama," he said slyly.

Livy looked at the dead flies, lying less than two inches from her food, swallowed hard, then asked a servant for a plate. Brushing the flies onto the plate with a napkin, she gave it to Jean and told her to take the flies into the parlor.

"You did beautifully, darling, and I'm very proud of you," she said. "I'll come and look at them as soon as we've finished dinner."

Jean walked carefully toward the door which led to the parlor, carrying her plate of flies, but was met by one of the cats, Sour Mash.

"Meearrrr! Meearrr!" begged the cat, putting his paws on Jean's dress.

"Sour Mash wants the flies, Mama," Jean called to her mother. "I think I'll give them to him. I know where I can get more."

It was not always easy for the children to distinguish between the laws of nature and those which governed their own lives. Jean and her Aunt Sue were in the garden at Quarry Farm one morning between breakfast and lunch. Several sparrows were pecking away at some seeds. Jean watched the birds for several minutes and then asked, "Doesn't it hurt the birds to eat between meals, Aunt Sue?"

The summers at Quarry Farm were restful but not uneventful. Livy's brother's family and her mother came out frequently from Elmira. On holidays, like the Fourth of July, there were fireworks on the lawn and picnics to adjoining woods.

When the summer was over and it was time to return to Hartford, Livy was always torn between anticipation of a return to their beloved home and a feeling of depression at leaving her relatives and friends in Elmira.

At the end of one summer, Livy, tired from packing the family belongings for the return trip and feeling melancholy over the leavetakings, went to her room at the end of the day to lie down and rest. They were to start for New York the next day, spend a few days there, and then go on to Hartford.

While Livy was resting, Susy came to her room, tiptoeing in. "Are you asleep, Mama?"

"No, darling."

"I wanted to show you something I made for Jean. It's for the train ride, so she won't be restless."

Livy sat up in bed, propping the pillows behind her. "Let me see, dear."

Susy came closer and produced a small bag she had

made. In it were paper dolls, cut out and ready for Jean to put faces on, some silk cloth, and a needle, thread, and buttons. Finally there was a scrapbook. Alongside each picture, Susy had written a little story.

"You blessed child!" Livy reached out to pull her oldest daughter close. It was so like Susy to be busy doing something for someone else, while she herself had been lying there giving in to sad thoughts.

"I'm going to get up now, dear, and we'll go outdoors before the light goes." Livy's spirits rose, and she began to look forward to the stay in New York. Samuel had tickets for a play and she had ordered a new dress, a soft gray satin, to wear to it. She always liked to look her best when they appeared together in public. She thought that she was not beautiful enough or wise enough to be the wife of the great Mark Twain.

But then, remembering the day the donkey sent him flying into the grass, Livy smiled. Mark Twain was also Sam Clemens and very much of a human being. He would be the first to say so.

Chapter Thirteen

"Mama, I can't make this veil hang right," Clara wailed to Livy. "How can I be Lady Jane if my veil is *all wrong?*"

Livy put down the piece of satin she was trying to drape around Susy's shoulders and picked her way between the costumes and scraps that were strewn all over the library, to where Clara struggled with yards of gauze. "Sit down, darling, and I'll fix it," Livy said. "Anyway, if everything is not just perfect for the dress rehearsal this afternoon, we'll have time to improve it before tomorrow night." She looked happily around her at the disordered room, her cheeks pink and her eyes sparkling. "Isn't it fun, darlings?" she asked.

"I can hardly wait to see Papa's face," Susy said. "Mama, do you think I speak my lines clearly? It would be terrible for the Prince to swallow his words."

"Of course you do, Susy. You have the gift of speech. Papa thinks you ought to become an actress, like Sarah Bernhardt—only I don't think actresses have too happy lives."

Susy's face flushed with pleasure at her mother's

compliment, and she bent her head over her work so that her expression was hidden. In a low voice, she said, "I think I would rather write books, like Papa."

"I shall be a famous pianist," said Clara, "and give concerts all over the world." She sat up straight and looked haughtily out over the room. "Gentlemen will fall at my feet and beg me to marry them but I shall say, 'No! I have my career!'"

Small Jean, too young for a part in the Clemens girls' dramatization of their father's book *The Prince and the Pauper,* was enjoying herself with a pair of blunt scissors and some scraps of cloth. She sat on the floor, humming to herself—a song, Livy noted with a tender smile, composed of the names of all the animals Jean knew.

The front door-knocker sounded and a few seconds later the servant George came into the library with a telegram from Sam. Livy hoped it would not say he was being delayed. The play, which she had put together from the book, was intended as a surprise for him on his expected arrival home the following evening. The Warners had offered their drawing room for the performance so chairs could be set up and a curtain arranged for ahead of time, without Samuel's knowing about it. Their daughter Daisy, a friend of the Clemens girls, was to play a part.

"Oh, my blessed darlings!" Livy exclaimed after she had read the wire. She looked distractedly about the room. "Start picking things up right away. Papa's coming home today, instead of tomorrow! He'll be here in a few hours." She put down the telegram, rang for Katy Leary and George, and began packing things up in boxes. "We'll take all this into the mahogany room for now," she said. "Papa seldom goes in there. I don't think we can manage a dress rehearsal at all; we will just have to give the play tomorrow night, mistakes and all."

The girls rushed about gathering up the costumes and paper and cloth. They had barely cleared the library of evidence when Sam's carriage wheels were heard outside.

"You children take Papa into the library while I take Daisy's costume to the Warners," Livy said, brushing at a wisp of hair which had fallen against her cheek. "I'll go out by the back door."

"He will come looking for you, Mama, you know that," Susy warned. "You must come back quickly."

Susy was right. Despite the cluster of daughters hanging on his arm, insisting on dragging him into the library where, Susy said, "We have a wonderful fire going, Papa, and lots to tell you," he kept looking for Livy.

"I am perspiring to hear it all," their father said, "but first I want to see Mama. Where is she?" Usually Livy met him at the door as eagerly as the children and he was puzzled and a little hurt.

"She's at the Warners', Papa, but she will be right back." Susy clung firmly to her father's arm. "Tell us about President Cleveland and how you rang all those bells when you went to visit him." This incident had been mentioned in a letter to the girls while their father was in Washington.

Controlling his impatience, Sam allowed himself to be seated in the library where he described in detail how he and some friends had gone to pay their respects to the newly-elected President of the United States. Growing tired of standing up, Sam had perched on the edge of a table. Suddenly, four young men appeared from four different directions and stood at attention.

"So the President told them," Sam finished his story, " 'Go away, gentlemen, no one needs you. Mr. Clemens just happens to be sitting on the call bells.' "

Livy came in as he was finishing the story, to the relief of the girls and of Sam.

For the rest of that day and all of the next, Susy and Clara and Daisy Warner were "on pins." They ran back and forth between the two homes with props and parts of costumes or to confer with Mrs. Warner. Fortunately, for most of the day Sam was absorbed in letters which had come while he was away, although Livy had to signal the girls twice to entertain their father while she sewed on buckles and made other last-minute preparations.

Finally, it was evening. Livy and Sam and the girls had their dinner, Sam grumbling some about having to go anywhere on his second evening at home. "I have all the company I need right here," he told his family. "Besides, it's been snowing and we'll all get wet feet."

"Oh, Papa, do stop objecting!" Susy cried out. She was tense with excitement and could scarcely swallow. Clara was not doing much better, she noticed.

When the Clemenses had crossed the hundred and fifty yards that separated their house from the Warners' and were ushered into the drawing room, it was to find a good-sized audience seated there. A place in the row directly in front of the curtain was vacant.

"That's for you, Sam," Charles Warner said, leading the now suspicious Sam to the vacant chair.

"Livy, what—" Sam began, looking around for his wife.

But Livy had disappeared. So had his daughters.

"Hush!" said Mr. Warner. "The show's going to begin in a few minutes."

When the curtain was drawn away, Susy, in the silks and satins of the Prince, and Daisy, dressed in the rags of Tom Canty, the Pauper, were revealed on a makeshift stage.

Mark Twain said of this evening that it was one of the loveliest of his life. Later he enlarged the part of Miles Hendon and played it himself when the play was put on again in the Clemens' own drawing room, as happened many times. He included parts for George Griffin and Katy Leary, too. Performances were sometimes given to an audience of eighty persons or more.

Susy and Clara and Daisy Warner liked to invent dramas of their own, also, especially those with queens as the main characters. They were fond of historical monarchs, like Elizabeth, and Mary, Queen of Scots. These dramas were given in their own playroom, with the girls parading about in some of Livy's old gowns. Meek, sweet-faced Jean, considered too young for a really important part, was given the job of drafting death warrants for the noble queens to sign. Scarcely able to use a pen, Jean sat patiently at her table performing her grisly task—unless, as often happened, she fell asleep. Sometimes when Jean was alone, Livy heard her putting on one of these dramas by herself, taking all the parts.

Mark Twain often underestimated his children's knowledge of him. Livy had a hard time making him watch his language in front of the children. One morning when they were all at breakfast, Livy criticized an acquaintance for using "strong language."

Susy and Clara piped up, "Why, Mama, Papa uses it, too!"

Sam was thunderstruck. He had thought the children unaware of his fiery vocabulary.

The girls adored their father, and yet were a little afraid of him. He could, by an unconscious severity of manner, make shy Susy shyer or intimidate even the more aggressive Clara. If he realized it, Livy thought often, he would have been hurt and troubled, so she did not tell him. She knew that Sam loved his children and her as much as or more than any man could love his family. She tried to help the children understand him and compensated for whatever wounds they received at his hands by being especially loving and understanding herself.

Livy was a firm disciplinarian and taskmaster, especially as far as the children's education was concerned, but she made learning as pleasant as possible. Their school year ended in June, before the family left for Quarry Farm, and examinations were given at that time. Together, Livy and the children gathered wild flowers and ferns from the woods and decorated the schoolroom for examination day. A few guests, mostly neighbors, were invited to come and hear the oral examinations given by the children's governess.

Susy Clemens was a child with remarkable gifts. At thirteen, she told the story of Cupid and Psyche in Latin as part of her school examination, and when she was seventeen, she wrote a two-act play, "A Love Chase," which impressed the adults in the audience with its language and music and dances. Her father described her on that occasion as radiant, in her dress covered with pink roses, her cheeks flushed, and her eyes shining brilliantly. She was slender, with plaits of copper hair hanging down her back. He said later that Susy at that age was the model for his portrait of the famous saint in his book *Joan of Arc*.

Susy also wrote a biography of her father. She began it when she was an adolescent and kept it up at intervals for years.

Susy's biography began: "We are a very happy family. We consist of Papa, Mama, Jean, Clara, and me.

It is Papa I am writing about, and I shall have no trouble in not knowing what to say about him, as he is a *very* striking character. . . . He is a very good man and a very funny one. He *has* got a temper, but we all of us have in this family."

Reading this, Livy laughed, but she felt a passing chagrin. Had she a temper, too?

"He is the loveliest man I ever saw or hope to see— and oh, so absent-minded. He does tell perfectly delightful stories," the biography went on.

One of Sam's favorite stories concerned his own absent-mindedness. He had to attend an authors' reception at the White House during Grover Cleveland's first term. Sam had met the President before, but not the President's wife, and Livy wanted to be sure he would not make any social errors.

When he was ready to leave Hartford for the trip to Washington, she walked with him to the door. Kissing him good-by, she said, "I've put a note in the vest pocket of your dress suit. You will find it when you are dressing for the reception because you always feel in your vest pockets." She didn't say for a cigar, but Sam knew what she meant. "Read that note and do what it says, please, darling, for me. I would tell you now what it says but I know you would not remember it for five minutes."

"Oh, Livy, Livy! You are a wonder." Sam caught her back into his arms for a second kiss and went out to his waiting carriage.

When he returned home a few days later, Livy asked, "Did you find my note?"

"Yes, darling, and I obeyed instructions. Here! I can prove it." Fishing out the calling card he had presented to Mrs. Cleveland when he greeted her, he handed it to Livy. On it was inscribed, in handwriting, "He did not. Frances F. Cleveland."

"Oh, Sam'l, you showed her my note!" Livy stared in wide-eyed dismay at her husband.

"It was all right, dearest. I didn't show it to her until *after* she had signed the card, although I had to do some good talking to get a blanket approval like that, sight unseen." Sam spoke very seriously, but laughter bubbled behind his gravity. Livy's note had instructed him to be sure not to wear his overshoes into the White House.

Sam was eventually shown Susy's biography. Several days after he had read it, Livy and Susy both became aware that he was trying very hard to be witty at the breakfast table.

When Livy and Susy were alone, later, Susy confided to her mother, "I think Papa was trying to say something remarkable for me to tell about in my biography of him."

Chapter Fourteen

Livy thoroughly enjoyed her role as wife and mother, but there was another part of her life that she treasured as much. This was her role as Sam's chief critic and editor. "You are the only critic I trust," Sam told her more than once. Livy, aware of her husband's remarkable talents, of the brilliance and beauty and power of his work, was sometimes frightened by her own responsibility. She sat by the hour, pencil in hand, reading both original manuscripts and proofs, praising what she thought was good, noting what she felt was unworthy of him.

"I hope you do right to trust me," she answered him. "I want only for you to do your best." Livy Clemens had never been afraid of responsibility and she accepted this one willingly, trusting Sam and her own instincts, knowing that not even for her would he change his work unless he believed her to be right. How much she loved him, she thought.

That her love was returned, she was never allowed to doubt. When she was nearing her fortieth and Sam

his fiftieth birthday, he left a note on the table by her
bed, after she was asleep.

"We have reached another milestone, my darling, &
a very remote one from the place whence we started;
but we look back over a pleasant landscape. . . . And
here we have company on the journey—ah, such precious company, such inspiring, such lovely & gracious
company . . . while they abide . . . our old love
grows and never diminishes . . ."

Livy, waking to the sun streaming into her room and
these words of warm devotion, lay for a few moments
thinking of her own good fortune. There was no one in
the world like her Sam'l, she thought. Even his faults
were endearing at times—like his absent-mindedness.
She had gone into the library a few days earlier and
found him roaring with laughter over a book.

"What are you reading, dear?" she asked, running an
affectionate hand through his hair.

He answered absently, "I didn't look at the title."

Livy, curious as to what writer could evoke so much
mirth from the witty Mark Twain, glanced over his
shoulder. The book, she saw, was one of Sam's own.

He was hopeless about anything mechanical. He
fought with the telephone after it was installed, swear-
ing many times a week that he would have it taken out.
A burglar alarm system which had been installed in the
Hartford house was another of his enemies. It never
worked, always going off at times when there was no

trespasser in the house. It went off one morning in March about two o'clock.

Half-asleep, Sam got up, went into the hall where the dial controlling the alarm system was, and glanced at the indicator. The needle pointed to the cellar door. Sam turned off the bell and went back to bed, not believing that anyone had broken in, by the cellar or any other way.

When he returned to bed, Livy said, "Maybe there really is a burglar this time, Sam'l. Which door was it?"

He told her, adding, "Of course it's a burglar. Nobody else ever comes in by the cellar door."

"Do you think he will take the silver?" Livy asked.

"There's nothing in the cellar except coal and vegetables. He's probably hungry and cold."

"Why don't you go down to the cellar and find out?"

"Oh, no," Sam said cheerfully. "I would much rather he picked out what he wants without my help."

"Sam'l, you are impossible!" But Livy nevertheless had to laugh. Even when the burglar alarm went off a second time, Sam merely got up and turned it off again. The dial now said the visitor was in the dining room.

When Sam arose the next morning, he found the gas lights burning on the first floor. An overcoat, new, an umbrella, old, and a pair of his shoes were missing. Following the burglar's trail through a wide open window, Sam found objects strewn along the man's escape avenue, but nothing of real worth had been taken. This, he

told Livy, was proof that he had been right in not bothering to interfere with the man.

Mark Twain's quirks and humors were mostly inten-
tional and Livy enjoyed them but there was another famous writer in Hartford whose eccentricities were sad-
dening. One warm summer day Livy's gardener came
to her and complained, "That Mrs. Stowe's gone and
done it again. She's picked all our finest flowers and gone
off with them."

Livy looked past him toward the gray-haired woman
going out through her garden gate with a handful of
prize blooms. She had been only seven years old when
Harriet Beecher Stowe's book *Uncle Tom's Cabin* was
published, but Uncle Tom, Eliza, and Little Eva seemed
like real persons to Livy. Now Mrs. Stowe was a neigh-
bor.

"You mustn't be angry with her, poor thing," tender-
hearted Livy told the gardener. "Let her do as she likes."
The once fine mind had deteriorated, and Mrs. Stowe
did not know what she was doing most of the time.

The gardener shook his head and walked off.

Livy thought about the first time Susy had encountered Professor Stowe, Harriet Stowe's husband, with
his long gray beard and his broad slouch hat. She had
come running home and exclaimed, "Mama, Santa Claus
has got loose!"

As Livy went back into the house, there was a distant
rumble of thunder. She looked apprehensively at the
sky. Lightning made a jagged stripe against the black

clouds. The children were over at the Warners. They were safe there.

Rain struck the windows and Katy Leary came to close a pair of French doors.

"This is going to be a dandy!" she said cheerfully, turning from the doors with her arms splashed with rain. Then, seeing Livy's white face, she said reassuringly, "Now, now, Mrs. Clemens—there's nothin' to fear. As long as you can see the lightning, you know it hasn't hit you."

"I know, Katy, but it terrifies me." She saw Samuel stepping out of the carriage, his head bare to every bolt of lightning.

"Oh, Sam'l," she said when he came in, "you promised me that you would always wear your hat in a storm. Now look at you."

He put a protective arm around her. "I've wished fifty thousand times in my life, whenever I made a fool of myself, that the lightning would strike me and I've never got anything out of it yet. I have missed several good chances." He brushed flecks of rain from his white waistcoat. "The storm will soon be over, honey."

Although he smiled and looked cheerful, there was worry in his face.

"Did you see Paige? How is the machine coming?" Livy asked. Sam had invested in a typesetting machine, invented by James W. Paige.

"It's going to be a regular miracle—only it needs more perfecting."

And more money, Livy thought to herself.

In 1884 Sam had started his own publishing company with his sister's son Charles Webster as manager. Former President Ulysses S. Grant was writing his memoirs and the new publishing house hoped to publish them. But as time went on the Webster Company hit snags.

The first of these was General Grant's failing health. Grant became so ill that writing with a pencil was impossible and Sam had to find a way for the aging man to finish his memoirs. He visited the ex-President daily when he was in New York and on one occasion, when Clara Spaulding and Susy and her mother were with him in the city, he took Susy along.

When Mark Twain and his daughter came into Grant's room, the famous man said with new hope in his voice, "I've been dictating this morning, Twain, and it was a great success."

"Good work, General!" Sam was delighted. Grant had insisted that he could never dictate what he had to say, but Sam had told him he was sure dictation would make things easier for him. Grant did not have much money, and both Sam and the general were concerned that money should be made from the memoirs. "Did you get down the Appomattox story?" Sam asked him.

"I did. You have no idea what a relief it is to me to be able to set the record straight on that one." The general coughed and cleared his throat which, since his illness, was often too congested to permit him to speak clearly. "And who is this young lady?" he asked, smiling at Susy.

Sam explained and then he and the general went on with their discussion of the memoirs.

When Susy got back to her mother and Clara Spaulding, she asked, "Is General Grant more famous than Papa?"

The two women laughed and then Livy said, "They are famous in different ways, dear. I don't think I can say any more than that."

Despite Sam Clemens' fears that Grant would die before he could finish his book, this did not happen. The book was completed and became a great success. So was Mark Twain's own *Huckleberry Finn*, published also by the Webster Company. The publishing venture was doing well until Sam looked around for other projects in which to invest part of the money he was making. One of these investments was the Paige typesetting machine.

"Couldn't we manage on the income from your writings, Sam'l?" Livy asked when he discussed this investment with her.

"But I would like to be free of all anxiety about you and the girls. My writing—well, if anything happens to me, the royalties from what has already been published will not go far. I want you to be secure, Livy, darling."

He was always trying to match the kind of background her father had provided, Livy thought, moved by her husband's pride and ambition. Knowing little of business matters, she said no more. All she wanted was to hold the happiness they had together with the children, safe from all threat.

Now, however, the typesetting machine was swallowing three thousand dollars a month; with its twenty thousand carefully adjusted parts, it was beginning to seem a monster that would consume all their reserves.

"It'll come out all right," Sam assured her. "There are millions to be made, Livy, darling. We just have to hold on—I'll find other financial backers if I have to."

With his damp lapel against her cheek, she said, "Yes, Youth. I know it will come out all right."

Chapter Fifteen

"ℋow brown things are getting in the garden," Livy said to Jean, pausing and looking out the window of the dining room. The two of them were on their way to the barn to have a look at Clara's cow, Jumbo. Sam and Clara had gone to Bryn Mawr to see Susy, who was enrolled there. "Soon it will be winter again. Autumn has seemed so short this year, especially since Susy went off to college."

"I wish it would snow right now." Ten-year-old Jean pressed her face to the window glass. "I haven't used the toboggan in such a long time."

Livy looked down at her youngest child. The family was growing up. Clara, who was sixteen, divided her time between her studies, long hours at the piano, and a busy social life. Susy, though beautiful, was awkward with young men, but Clara was already very popular. Thinking of this, and of Susy, Livy's thoughts grew anxious. It was Susy's own decision to go to Bryn Mawr so Sam had taken her there one rainy, dreary day in August. When he returned, he told Livy that Susy was crying when he left her but not to worry. "She'll master life there in no time," he had declared cheerfully.

Susy had mastered her school work easily enough, because she had a brilliant mind. But like many talented children, she was emotional and intense and idealistic. Susy took herself and life very seriously. Livy thought that this might be her fault. She and her eldest daughter had always been extremely close and Susy had probably absorbed her mother's idealism—an idealism that Livy had clung to but which, at times, had come up against some severe shocks.

But it was not just inherited idealism and sensitivity that was Susy's problem, Livy knew. Susy had a genius for a father; despite her talents and giant ambition, it must sometimes seem hopeless to diffident Susy that she could ever achieve a place for herself that would compare with that of Mark Twain. Clara was different. Clara lived for the day when she could go to Europe and study with a distinguished music teacher, confident that she would become a great pianist.

Susy's letters home from Bryn Mawr had tried to sound cheerful but Livy had read the homesickness between the lines. "I wonder if she should stay," she said to Sam when Susy had been gone two months. "She is not strong, and unhappiness might make her ill."

"Livy, darling," Sam had protested, "Susy is eighteen years old. She must stand on her own feet."

But for both his and Livy's sake, he had decided to go and see Susy, taking Clara with him. They were due back from Bryn Mawr today. A letter from Sam said he had gone to a dance given at Susy's boarding house, dancing the Virginia reel twice. The rheumatism which had been bothering him had let up for a few days.

It was clear that Samuel had enjoyed himself, Livy had thought when she read his letter, but what of Susy? Had Susy danced, too, or had she stood on the sidelines as usual?

Jean touched her mother's arm. "Come on, Mama. Jumbo expects us." Jean had promised Clara, when she left, that she would keep an eye on her sister's pet —actually Clara had outgrown Jumbo. She had only been trying to please Jean. Clara had raised the cow from a calf, because Patrick McAleer had told her if she washed and curried it properly it would grow up into a pony. Jumbo had failed to perform this miracle, but the girls loved the animal, anyway.

"All right, darling," Livy said.

Walking with Jean through the rooms of her beloved house, Livy tried to dispel the melancholy which too often assailed her when Samuel was away. Part of her depression was concern over their financial troubles. Samuel had been unable to raise capital for the still un-perfected Paige typesetter the last time it was needed, so she had persuaded him to borrow from her inheritance. But still the machine was not ready. The Webster Publishing Company was faltering. Charles Webster was not well. Sam was working on a new book, *A Connecticut Yankee at King Arthur's Court*, but it was hard going.

"Slow down, dear," Livy said to Jean as they emerged from the house and headed toward Jumbo's shed. It was tiresome to be so easily fatigued, she thought impatiently, but her breath was coming too slowly. She was afraid.

Inside the barn with its mixed smell of hay and manure, Livy watched Jean stroke the cow's nose for several minutes. A pale light filtered through the barn window, falling across the silky head of the little girl. Jean leaned forward and kissed the cow's none-too-clean neck. "Would you like to kiss Jumbo, too, Mama?" she asked.

Livy burst into laughter, dispelling her own gloom. "No, thank you, darling. One kiss is all Jumbo needs."

Later, after Sam and Clara had returned and the two girls were in bed, Livy asked her husband, "Youth, dear, is Susy really happy at college? I know you said she laughed and talked and was very glad to see you and Clara—but was she settled into the life there?"

Sam picked up the pages of manuscript Livy had attempted to read through before he came home in order to discuss it with him. He paced back and forth across the room for a few minutes, carrying the sheets but not looking at them, finally stopping beside Livy's chair. "There's no use trying to fool you, Livy. Clara and I had a fine time—but Susy doesn't. She misses you too much. But I think she should stick it out as long as she wants to."

They talked a while about other things. Theo Crane had died the year before and Livy had just had a letter from Sue, saying how lonely she was at Quarry Farm. Sam gave a discouraging report on his attempts to raise money. "The national depression doesn't help," he said.

"I try to economize," Livy said with a sigh, "but money seems to vanish just the same. I suppose we should not have bought those bicycles, but Jean always seems to be left out of things. I thought if you and she learned to bicycle together, she would be pleased."

"*If* we learn is right," Sam said. He had as little talent for riding a bicycle as he had for riding a donkey. His daughters and Livy had already enjoyed good laughs at his expense.

Livy held out her arms to him. "Pull me up, Youth. We ought to go to bed ourselves. You must be tired from your journey and I'm tired from waiting." She smiled at him, but there were dark circles under her eyes. She wished that Sam had bundled up Susy and brought her home with him.

Susy stayed at Bryn Mawr until spring but then asked to come home. Livy went to help her eldest pack her belongings and withdraw from college.

As the train wheels clacked under them on the homeward journey, Susy said, "I am so ashamed, Mama. I am almost nineteen years old and ought to be a mature person by now. I keep wishing I could be like Aunt Sue —so poised and gracious to everyone." She turned a flushed face toward her mother. "I'm going to get control of myself, Mama, some way. I have been reading again about mind cures and perhaps there is something in them that will help me. Jean said it helped her stomach aches."

"It will surely do no harm to have a cheerful and positive attitude," Livy said. She remembered Dr. Newton's admonitions to her when she started to walk again after her accident. She put a hand over Susy's. "We are all so happy that you are coming home. It has been a sad year, with both Grandma Clemens and Grandma Langdon leaving us forever." Sam's mother had died in October and Livy's only a month later. "As for your education, Papa thinks we will really go to Europe this year. Aunt Sue will go with us; she wants to hear and see the Bayreuth Festival with us."

Susy brightened. "That will be wonderful! Oh, I can hardly wait to start. Think of it, Papa and you and Clara and Jean and Aunt Sue and Katy—all of us traveling together." She added thoughtfully, after a second, "It will be cheaper living in Europe, won't it?"

"We hope so." The children knew about the typesetting machine; it had shadowed their lives, too, for the past few years. At times it had seemed to be completed—it had, in fact, been tried and had set type faster than anyone had dreamed possible. A year ago Sam himself had set the name of William Shakespeare in type on it, forgetting the "e" at the end, and had been so delighted with the machine that he had been wild with hope. But the machine had developed new, mechanical problems, as it always did, and needed more money. Livy and Sam had borrowed everywhere they could and Sam had given up hope of borrowing more for the present. The machine would have to wait.

Poor Youth, Livy thought. A few years ago he had been so sure that everything he touched would turn to gold. Now it seemed the opposite was true. They would have to close the house while they were away, because it cost too much to keep it going—perhaps they could find someone to lease it later. Sam was so busy that it would be up to her to take care of the details about the house—temporary positions must be found for George Griffin and Patrick McAleer, until the family came back. Only Katy Leary, who was almost a member of the family, would go with them to Europe.

Fortunately, Sam was working hard on a new novel. And he was hoping to get a newspaper syndicate to sign up for a series of letters on Europe, to help with their expenses.

"I wish Papa had never met Mr. Paige!" Susy burst out suddenly.

"Sometimes I do, too," Livy said.

Before the Clemenses left for Europe, Sam agreed to let a painter, Charles Noel Flagg, do a portrait of him. He liked to sit for his portrait, claiming he got more information out of the artist while he smoked and chatted with him than he could get from several books on art. One day, when the portrait was almost finished, Livy and Sue Crane came to Mr. Flagg's studio to have a look at it.

"It's fine," Livy said, studying the painting from several angles, "except that Sam'l's tie is crooked."

"It always is," the artist said.

And Sam told her, "If you were to make that necktie straight people would say, 'Good portrait, but there is something the matter with it.'"

Livy yielded and the portrait was painted with Sam's tie hanging at the familiar angle.

A much less pleasant event also occurred before the European excursion could get under way. Charles Webster, the manager of Sam's publishing firm, died. The business was already tottering. Sam replaced his nephew with another manager and hoped for the best, but he had a feeling that his luck in business had very nearly run out.

"I want to get out of here," he said to Livy. "The girls and you and I and Sue Crane will all be better off in Europe for a time." His rheumatism had been so bad of late that he had tried to use a dictating machine but had given up, finding that it took him much longer than when he used his pen, even with a stiff arm.

The Clemens party, with twenty-five trunks, sailed on a French ship to Le Havre in June of 1891, leaving only the gardener and his wife in charge of the house which had been home to them for seventeen years. At the last moment, Livy walked alone through the rooms, saying a silent good-by to it, not knowing when she would see it again.

Chapter Sixteen

The tiny cafe on one of the side streets of Bayreuth, Germany, where the music festival honoring Richard Wagner was being held, was jammed with people. Livy looked at the frankfurter on her plate with distaste. This was the third time they had been served frankfurters in the past four days.

"Come on, swallow a few bites, or I refuse to take you to the show," Sam coaxed her from his place on the other side of the cafe table.

"Don't call a Wagnerian opera a show, Papa," Clara objected. The Clemenses, plus Sue Crane and Katy Leary, were sitting almost in each other's laps, because of the scarcity of space in the town.

To please Sam, Livy forced herself to eat the spicy sausage and swallow a bit of bread. Poor food and crowded lodgings, even the jostling on the streets, didn't really matter, she thought. She was delighted to be there. So were the girls and Sue. It was very exciting. Half the world seemed to have come to hear the great operas in the opera house in the mountains, from ordinary, average citizens to royalty attired in rich costumes and bedecked with jewels.

The family finished the meal and Sam urged them outside. "You wouldn't want to miss a single note," he teased them. He had little liking for classical music but had bought tickets for the famous festival for his family's pleasure.

Livy took her husband's arm as they walked across the sidewalk to the carriage Sam had hired. She looked up into his face and said, "If it is dreadfully tiresome to you, darling, you wouldn't need to come with us today. We will get back to the pension safely enough."

Sam grinned at her. "If you women can stand it day after day, I can. I'm probably the strongest man around."

Susy, one foot on the carriage step, turned to say, "No, you are not, Papa. Siegfried is the strongest. He slew the dragon, Fafnir."

Her father gave her ear a light pinch. "That is just something a writer made up," he said, following her up the steps, telling the driver to start off.

As their carriage stopped outside the great building sunk low in its rim of mountains and they dismounted, Katy Leary stared at the carriage ahead of theirs. "Them horses have gold harnesses!" she whispered to Livy. "Real gold!"

"I know," Livy said. She tugged at Katy's sleeve. "It's rude to stare, Katy."

"It doesn't do any good, anyway," Clara said. "The royalty covers itself up so you can't see anything except their noses."

The performance took place in the center of the

opera ring, below the tiers of seats. Sue, Livy, and the
three girls were all caught up in the tide of glorious
music that rose up from the stage and orchestra pit, but
Sam found he spent more time watching the audience
and listening to their comments than he did enjoying
the music. He decided that it would be impossible for
him to cultivate a taste for opera. He did, however, enjoy watching Livy and his daughters and their beloved
Aunt Sue while they listened.

After a summer spent in visiting health resorts and
spas, Sam, Livy, and Sue Crane decided to spend the
winter in Berlin. They lived for two months in a ground
floor apartment in an unpretentious part of the city
and then moved to the Hotel Royal.

Livy, realizing that in spite of their economic problems, they were still living too lavishly, decided to send
Katy Leary home for the winter. It was time for the
girls to learn to pack and unpack their trunks by themselves anyway.

"It is really impossible to live very cheaply if you
are Mark Twain," Livy said to Sue Crane one day,
frowning over a pile of bills. "Everyone in Berlin seems
to know Sam'l and want to entertain him. We have to
have clothes for these affairs. And the girls must be edu-
cated." She picked up a bill for piano instruction and
laid it down again. "Susy and Clara could never have
such teachers, even for twice that amount, at home."

"They both have too much talent for their training to be neglected," Sue Crane agreed. Her hair had begun to gray but her face still wore the look of gentle kindness which had always distinguished it. "Jean—" She stopped, looked doubtful, as if not quite sure how to proceed.

"Sue, I don't know what to do for Jean," Livy said. "She feels so badly because she has no special gift. It does no good for me to tell her that her talent is kindness and a loving heart. Jean wants something more, something, I suppose, that will impress her father."

Sue glanced down at the newspaper spread beside her on the sofa. "He seems to have been his usual successful self last night, judging from this account. Was it late when you got back to the hotel?"

"Two o'clock," Livy said. "And now Sam has a bad cold. The night air was freezing and the lecture room was too hot. And then we had to attend General von Versen's ball afterward."

As a result of that evening, Sam was confined to his bed with a lung congestion for an entire month. Medical bills seemed to be a part of the Clemenses' life. Sam's arm, Livy's heart, Susy's delicate health that bent under any passing blow, and Jean's stomach-aches and head-aches, all required attention. Only Clara seemed to be strong, although as a child she had often been ill.

During his convalescence, Sam was not forgotten by German friends. When he was able to receive callers,

Emperor William II of Germany sent the wife of General von Versen to the Clemenses' apartment with an invitation for Sam to come to a flag ceremony in the palace. On learning that Sam was not yet well enough to attend, the Emperor asked Frau von Versen to arrange a dinner for Mark Twain, himself, and a few other guests at the earliest date Sam would be well enough.

"Goodness, Papa, will you know what to say to the Emperor?" Susy asked her father when this message was brought to him.

Sam looked slyly at Livy. "No—but your Mama will tell me."

"Now, Sam'l—" Livy's cheeks turned pink. He was always teasing her because she worried so much that he might make a mistake in etiquette. "I only tell you about mistakes because you say you wish me to."

He grinned, and looking over Livy's bent head at Susy and Clara, said, "Sometimes I only make mistakes for the pleasure of hearing your mother scold me."

The doctor decided that Sam should go to a warmer climate so he and Livy left the children in Berlin with Sue and set out for the south of France. Mentone was warm and quiet and they felt almost like honeymooners, alone in such a pleasant spot. Livy had acquired a camera and enjoyed taking pictures as she and Sam strolled about the town.

"I think you're taking one picture right on top of another," Sam told her, watching the performance.

"I am not!" Livy aimed her camera at him. "I shall just take you wearing that scowl and show it to everyone."

Sam's arm continued to bother him despite the mild climate. He thought he could not write, but with Livy's help, he managed to keep up the work that had to be done. They went on to Rome and then to Florence, where they rented the beautiful Villa Viviani for the following year.

The villa was a plain, square building of light yellow with green shutters, standing on a rise of ground overlooking orchards, vineyards, and in the distance, the city of Florence. Full of windows, the twenty-eight or more rooms of the house were filled with sunshine when the Clemens family walked into it.

"Oh, Mama, Papa, it's heavenly!" Susy said, walking almost on tiptoe over the shining floors. She crossed to a door which opened onto a balcony overlooking a terrace and took deep breaths of the sweet air. "Do come out here," she called to the others.

Sam, Livy, and Jean followed her, leaving Clara prowling around the huge salon in the center of the house. From the terrace, they could see roses spilling over the mossy urns on the gateposts and over garden walls.

"This is royal living," Livy said, "and at only half

what it would cost to live at home." She hoped that no one heard the wistful note in her voice as she pronounced the last word. She refused to allow herself to feel homesick in this beautiful place.

Clara finally came out and joined the rest of the family. "There must be plenty of servants," she said. "I went into the dining room and the table is all laid. I never thought we should live in a palace, did you, Susy?"

Susy shook her head. "Let's take a walk through the gardens before dinner, Clara. Jean, do you want to come, too?"

Sam and Livy stayed on the terrace watching, as the three girls wandered among the roses below them. Neither of them said anything for some time and then Sam said, "We ought to get a dog or some cats for Jean."

Livy turned and put her head against his shoulder. "We'll get a dog for Jean and cats for you, darling. That's what you really mean."

The villa came staffed with well-trained servants, so Livy had little to do except rest, usually on the balcony overlooking the terrace. At the sunset hour, the great ball of warmth settled down behind the hills in a flood of light that both comforted and inspired her.

Sam was writing again, swiftly and furiously, and this knowledge made Livy deeply happy. Listening con-

tentedly to the scratch of his pen, Livy prayed that
the new book about Joan of Arc would be all that Sam
hoped for. He was going to publish it anonymously, he
said, because it was a serious book and no one took Mark
Twain seriously. He had started the book several times
but had agreed with Livy that none of the starts was
good enough. Now he had begun again.

Clara was the only restless one in the villa that fall.
She had been studying music at Mrs. Willard's School
in Berlin and felt that she ought to continue if she was
ever to become a great pianist.

Sam and Livy let her go back and become a boarding
student at the school. When, however, Clara wrote from
Berlin that she did not want to come to Florence for
Christmas, Livy found this hard to bear. The family
had always been together for Christmas. But she wrote
to her daughter that she must do whatever seemed right
to her for her career.

"I only hope that she is thinking more of her career
than of a good time," Livy said to Susy and Jean, after
a letter that told of the balls, operas, and concerts Clara
had been invited to.

"Yaas will watch out for her, Mama, even though he
does tease terribly," Susy said. "Yaas" was her nickname
for Mr. William Phelps, the American ambassador to
Berlin, who was a close friend of the Clemenses. The
nickname came from the way Mr. Phelps pronounced
"Yes." "Besides, Clara always knows what to do. . . ."

Susy was busy arranging a bouquet of flowers as she spoke.

"Well, but she tells of being alone with forty officers! I shall ask Papa to write her very sternly when he returns from this last trip home," Livy said. The continuing troubles of both the publishing firm and the typesetter kept forcing Sam to make trips to America to try to save himself from financial ruin, so that Livy and the two girls were alone in Florence much of the time.

When Sam returned, he reported that it was only a matter of time until his publishing company would go under.

"I'm not a businessman," he confessed to Livy. "I've not got the nature or disposition for it and I'm tired, tired of it. I want to get out."

"If we can get out with honor, dear, I am willing." Livy, whose health had grown worse despite the balmy climate, watched her beloved Youth pace the floor, her heart sore with pity.

They closed the villa in June and went to Franzenbad, Germany, in the hope that the baths would improve Livy's health. Clara, now a graduate of Mrs. Willard's, would join them in Munich, but Susy wished to go to Paris.

"I want to study voice with Madame Marchesi," Susy said. Susy had a soprano voice of great charm.

Livy looked at this daughter for whom she felt, sometimes guiltily, such a great well of love, and wondered if she could bear to be separated from Susy again, or

Susy from her. But she said, "If Papa agrees, you may go, darling."

As she spoke, Livy's heart fluttered, jumping queerly. She pressed her hand against her breast, waiting for the pain to pass.

Chapter Seventeen

$\mathcal{S}$am's reunion with the family in Europe did not last. He was called again to the United States. Clara, who had been unable to get rid of a bothersome cough, was to go with him.

"The ocean voyage will do you good," Livy said. She still felt a wrench each time the family had to be separated but it was easier to release Clara, the self-sufficient one of her three daughters, than either Susy or Jean. And Sam needed someone to cheer him on the dreadful voyages back and forth across the ocean. He was sandwiching in whatever writing he could that would bring immediate returns, setting aside the Joan of Arc story for the time being. Livy thought that he might be doing work which was beneath him, because of the financial pressures, but there was little she could do about it.

Susy's brief trip to Paris had resulted in discouragement. Madame Marchesi had told her that she had an unusual voice. "Very good, very pure, she said it was," Susy reported to the family when she joined them at

Franzenbad. "But she will not give me lessons. I am too frail in body, Madame said."

Susy crossed to where a mirror hung and studied her slight figure gloomily. "She said it took great physical stamina to practice long hours as an opera singer must." "Then we will have to see that you grow strong and healthy," Livy said. Susy was still the same wisp of a girl who had come back so despondently from Bryn Mawr. Livy wondered if she would ever be different.

After Sam and Clara left for the United States, Livy took Jean and Susy and moved to Paris. There was cholera in Germany and Sam wanted them out of it. Livy took rooms at the Hotel Brighton and settled down to wait for Sam's letters and his eventual return to Paris.

Susy, having spent time at the baths as recommended by Madame Marchesi, went back to the famous teacher and was given lessons for a time, although she was still not really strong enough. Teachers were secured for Jean, also, and the girls' and Livy's social life was filled with concerts, theater parties, and dinners at the homes of Sam's Paris friends.

Clara came back to Europe before her father, bringing news of Elmira and amusing stories about Sam. But Livy knew the strain Sam was under. He had written that the publishing company could not be saved, but there was hope for the typesetting machine. Also, Sam had made a new friend, an oil magnate named H. H. Rogers. Mr. Rogers, without compensation, had offered to take charge of Sam's financial affairs and try to salvage what he could from the mess.

On April 18 of that year, 1894, the Webster Publishing Company failed.

"Our only hope now," Sam wrote Livy, "is the typesetter."

He came back to Paris in May, and shortly afterward, Mr. Rogers wrote him that the machine was at last completed and was being given a long, thorough trial at the *Times-Herald* newspaper in Chicago.

"The worst is over, Livy," Sam said after this letter arrived. He waved the sheet of paper in the air jubilantly. "We've pulled through, my darling, and from here on it will be writing for me and peace and quiet for you."

The Clemenses spent the following winter in Paris, Sam devoting himself once more to what he thought of as a labor of love, his book about Joan of Arc.

The whole family was caught up in the work. Each day he read what he had written to Livy and the girls. Susy was so wrapped up in the book that she seemed almost to be suffering Joan's agonies.

During the pages describing Joan's trial, Susy would interrupt her father's reading, saying, "Wait, wait till I get a handkerchief!"

When the final pages were read, Susy wrote in her diary, "Tonight Joan of Arc was burned at the stake."

They rented the studio home of an artist for the winter. Livy would much rather have gone home to

Hartford, but their income still did not permit them to operate such an expensive house. They had leased it to people whom Sam had told her loved it almost as much as they had themselves.

The Paris house was tastefully furnished and they all enjoyed it. Sam was writing well and with absorption, Susy's health was better than it had been in a long time, and they had many interesting friends in Paris.

Livy, also stronger than she had been, gave a series of dinner parties. She said to Susy one day while they were making out a guest list, "What are we going to do about making Papa remember his duties as host? Last week, when the Gilberts were here, he nearly talked Mrs. Gilbert to the death and paid no attention at all to the lady on his right."

"Jean and Clara and I were talking to Papa about that," Susy said. "He says it is no good your reminding him after the party is over. You have to remind him while the party is going on."

"I can't do that, dear, in front of the guests."

"Papa has worked out a sort of code. When he talks too much to one lady, you will say a sentence to him that has the words 'blue card' in it. When he is not talking at all to anyone and should be, the signal is 'red card.' "

Livy looked up from her writing and released one of her rare peals of laughter. "I don't believe it will work but we can try it."

The signal system did work, however, according to

Mark Twain. If Livy was too busy with her own social duties to notice him, she would be reminded by one of the girls. They stationed themselves behind a screen within earshot of Livy but out of sight of the guests. "Blue card" or "red card," one of them would hiss to their mother.

In October, Sam received a copy of the first paragraphs set by the typesetting machine. He was overjoyed and said that he felt like Columbus when he first saw land. The machine had set type for eight hours with only seventeen minutes of stoppage.

It was the last good news of a business nature that the Clemenses received. The stoppages increased to such a point that the *Times-Herald* gave up using the typesetter. By Christmas it was all over, and Sam Clemens was a ruined man financially. He did not go home because Mr. Rogers was handling his affairs better than he could have himself.

"I have to finish *Joan*," he said to Livy, "and I can do it better here than there, as long as Rogers doesn't need me." He took Livy's hand in his. "I meant to take such wonderful care of you," he said, and there was a break in his voice, "but all I have brought you is anxiety and failure."

"Youth, darling, don't, please. You have brought me the tenderest love and the greatest devotion any woman ever received. All I care about now is that we climb out of this dark pool with honor. I want us to face the world without shame. Every single penny of what we owe those good people who trusted us must be paid back, Sam'l. I will never rest until that has been accomplished."

Sam let her hand drop.

"It's impossible, Livy," he said flatly. "I'm old. One day, back in New York, I overheard a group of rich men talking. They said a man of fifty-eight can't get up again, after a real failure. Maybe they weren't talking about me, but it's true of me. I can try, but I won't make it."

Livy pulled him down to sit beside her. "Darling, they were *not* talking about you! Nobody could talk about Samuel Langhorne Clemens with anything except admiration and belief. Remember a little while ago you mentioned a lecture tour—I'd go with you. We could all go—Susy, Clara, Jean—all of us."

Sam bit the end off a cigar, lit it, and blew a great cloud of smoke across the room. "It might mean years, Livy. It would have to be a world tour."

Livy reached for the pad and pencil that she had kept at hand ever since their economic problems had begun. She calculated carefully, adding and subtracting. Finally she looked up. "It shouldn't take more than four years to pay our debts, if we went on a big lecture tour. You say Mr. Rogers does not want us to sell the Hartford house unless we have to. Look, Sam'l, if we do it this way, we will not have to."

He studied her calculations. His face brightened. "I

believe you're right, Livy. We could do it—or I reckon we could give it a good, hard try." He put his arm around her and said earnestly, "There's not your match to be found anywhere when it comes to foresight, wisdom, accurate calculation, and good judgment—except for Mr. Rogers."

They told the girls about the plan at dinner that evening.

"Then we'll be poor for a long time yet," Clara said resignedly.

"I won't mind that, if only we could stay in Paris." It was Susy speaking. "I mean, I would like to go home if we were going to stay there in our own house, but traveling all over the world—" She gave a shiver of distaste.

It had been a wonderful winter for Susy, Livy knew. Sam and Susy had spent hours together, discussing his work—especially *Joan of Arc*—and going on from that to discussions of philosophy and religion and art. Sam encouraged Susy to keep up her interest in mental health, thinking it had helped her. He treated Susy as a contemporary, respecting her fine, serious mind.

Sam sailed for home in March, returning in May to get his family. The United States was full of the news of Mark Twain's bankruptcy, and Livy, to whom financial failure was a disgrace, found it hard to bear. They went as soon as possible to Quarry Farm.

"It is hard not to think of going to Hartford and our own house," Livy said to Sue Crane a few days after their arrival at the farm, "but it's wonderful to be here with you again."

"The studio is just the way Sam left it," Sue said, "except that more vines have grown up over it." She was as happy to have her sister and brother-in-law home as they were to be there.

At that moment Jean came in, her face radiant. "Oh, Aunt Sue, everything is just the same. I just went out to see Ellerslie and it looks absolutely darling. Now I know we're really home."

Ellerslie, Livy thought. She had almost forgotten about the little house her sister had had constructed for the girls, when they were younger. Ellerslie, named after a house in one of the girls' favorite books, was a complete cottage in miniature, with a porch, a tiny stove, dishes, tables, chairs, and a broom. Over the years of their growing up, the girls, especially Susy, had used Ellerslie as a place to be alone when they felt the need of solitude, and a place to play when they wanted company. It was also the favorite place of the cats, sometimes as many as eleven in number.

Livy, seeing the light on her youngest daughter's face at finding Ellerslie again, felt her heart throb painfully. The girls were so happy to be settled at the farm—how could she take them away again? But she would have to, for Sam's sake. Take them—or leave them behind. She pushed that thought away, refusing it.

Chapter Eighteen

*T*he electric light over the railroad platform at Elmira gleamed feebly in contrast to the great stars overhead. July heat spread over the surrounding fields and the cry of crickets could be heard above the panting of the locomotive as it steamed slowly away.

Livy stood beside Sam and Clara on the rear observation platform of the train, her gaze clinging to the lonely-looking figures under the electric light.

Clara called out, "We'll see you in Europe next year, Susy!"

Livy's throat tightened. This was not how they had planned the world lecture tour. She had always expected that the whole family, including Katy, would go. But Susy, Jean, and Katy were staying behind, Susy to rest and grow strong at Quarry Farm with her aunt, Jean to attend a preparatory school in Elmira, and Katy to take care of them.

"Good-by—good-by!" Livy cried, the words stinging her throat as tears stung her eyelids. How frail and tense Susy looked.

"Susy will be fat as a Wagnerian prima donna next time we see her, Mama," Clara said comfortingly.

Livy threw a kiss to Jean.

Sam's hand gripped his wife's elbow and she leaned against him. At least she was feeling well, and able to withstand the rigors of the long journey ahead. She was in better health than Sam, just now. He was still weak from an attack of bronchitis and was suffering from a painful carbuncle.

Night closed over the landscape and the three travelers, able to see the station no longer, went inside the train.

Through the July heat they crossed Ohio, Minnesota, and Dakota into the rolling vastness of Montana, Sam performing night after night at stops along the way. On the train Sam sometimes wore a nautical cap perched on his bushy, silver hair. Livy tried to imagine him as a youthful river pilot with self-confidence and jaunty assurance as he listened for the leadsman's call of "Mark Twain!"—the riverman's signal that had given Sam the idea for his *nom de plume*. Sam had come a long way from that time of riding up and down the dark, liquid road of the Mississippi, she thought. He seemed cheerful, but Livy knew that he faced their arduous journey with doubt and dread. Did he have regrets, yearn back for that simpler life he had left so long ago? She did not know.

The tour was an overwhelming success from the start. The Clemenses were deluged with flowers, driven

in expensive vehicles to lecture halls, and applauded
wherever they appeared.

In response to Clara's enthusiastic letters home, Susy
wrote, "Poor little modest Mama! I suppose she is learning to put up with much splurge."

Susy reported that life in Elmira was uneventful except for watching a baseball game or going to a band
concert. There had been a dance in town but she was,
as usual, a wallflower. For Susy, the planned meeting
in England was "beautiful and golden and alluring,"
and she said, "When the time comes to start toward her,
I will throw up, *up* my hat!" By "her" she meant Livy.

On shipboard, sailing from Vancouver toward the
Hawaiian Islands, Sam grew more optimistic about the
future. He had always loved ships and the sea. In the
evenings, he, Livy, and Clara studied the stars by tele-
scope or played a card game with the captain and other
ship's officers. When Sam grew too excited over the
games, Livy had to exercise all her powers of persuasion
to keep him from exploding.

"Youth, dear," she would say in an undertone, "getting in a temper won't help you win."

"I don't care a rap about beating," he said, "but I
can't stand the sight of such cards. They make me boil
—only a saint on ice could keep cool."

Beyond the Hawaiian Islands, they encountered flying fish which enchanted Livy. She wrote to Jean about
them.

Both Livy and Sam were keenly aware of their stake

in the success of the tour. Livy, especially, would not rest until all debts were paid. Sam's lectures were averaging two hundred dollars a performance, which made them hopeful.

"Perhaps it will not take four years to get clear," Livy said to Sam. "Won't we celebrate, though, on the day that last dollar is paid back!"

When they reached the harbor of Sydney, Australia, newspaper reporters, photographers, and Mark Twain fans crowded the pier to greet them. Almost before she had time to take off her hat, Livy was busy in her hotel room answering letters and greetings they found waiting for them, with Clara helping her.

Livy and Clara were Sam's first critics. After each lecture when the three of them were alone in their hotel quarters, he would ask them how the lecture had sounded.

"Papa, you don't need to ask us how good you were, with all Sydney applauding you," Clara said.

"That's true," Livy said. And then added, "But I do think that second pause—in the story about grandfather's ram—could be a trifle longer."

"I wondered why they didn't laugh at that point," Sam said. "I surmise you're right, Livy. Again. We'll slow that down a trifle."

The tour through southern climates had less pleasant aspects. Livy learned to shake out her clothing before she dressed, in case a giant cockroach or spider might be hidden in the folds. Sam, wakened by a roach walking over his face one night, insisted it had been an alligator.

He continued to be a success, however, and they sent regular, substantial payments to Henry Rogers for application against their debts.

One of Sam's first lectures in Bombay was before an audience of purdah women behind a curtain. Livy, wanting to have a look at the costumes of rich native women, went to a museum one morning between ten and twelve o'clock, a time when no men were allowed in the galleries.

The Indian women were beautifully dressed. Every part of the museum, even up to the second floor balconies, was filled with the sparkle of silk and jewels.

Livy was as much a curiosity to the Indian women as they were to her. Chattering and exclaiming, they examined every detail of her costume, from her veil to the white bugle beads on her green satin dress, to the tips of her shoes.

Not used to so much close attention, Livy tried to escape behind display cases and into other rooms, but the women followed her. Not understanding Hindustani, Livy pointed to her mouth and shook her head, to indicate she did not know what they were saying.

One woman said, then, in English. "Why do you wear that?" She pointed to Livy's veil. "It makes black spots on your face."

The woman who had spoken was covered with her own kind of spots—tattoo marks.

The Clemens trio spent over two months in India, going from there to South Africa. When they reached Durban, Livy and Clara settled down for a rest and let Sam go on alone to lecture at other South African cities. All three of them were looking forward now to the reunion with Susy, Jean, and Katy in England on August 12.

Livy, during the long days and nights under a South African sky, thought deeply about her children and herself and Sam. Had she adored him too much? Surely she had loved her children just as much, if differently, as she had her husband. Lily Warner had once chided her, saying that Livy demanded too much of both herself and others. Perhaps, Livy thought, because at one time she had not hoped to marry, she was greedy, asking for a perfection of family life that was unattainable on this earth. The chances were good that Samuel would outlive her. Would he understand the children, know how to help them to be happy? Susy had written that she was growing very strong and could practice singing for several hours without getting tired. Jean's letters, too, sounded cheerful.

Livy asked Sam one day if he thought she had been too demanding as a wife and mother.

"Why, Livy," he said. "You are so dear and good and steadfast and fine—"

It was no use. She put her finger against his lips. "You are completely prejudiced," she said.

That Mark Twain was sincere in his respect for and devotion to his wife was demonstrated when Harper and Brothers published *Joan of Arc*. The book, although published anonymously in magazine form, was soon recognized as Sam's work. When it was published in book form, he dedicated it to Livy. It was, in his opinion, the only book he had written which was worthy of her.

Chapter Nineteen

Sam and Livy and Clara arrived in England the last day of July, 1896. They had been on their tour for thirteen months.

In the small house they had rented in Guildford, near London, Livy stood looking around, wondering if it would be large enough when Susy, Jean, and Katy arrived.

Clara stood pulling at her fingers. "I'll never be a pianist, Mama!" she complained. "My fingers are too short. I think I'll become a singer, like Susy. We can sing duets." Clara drew closer to her mother. "I can't wait until their ship arrives, can you?"

"We must be patient, Clara. It is only August the fifth. There are seven more days."

"You should speak to Papa about patience! He keeps going out to buy more flowers for everyone's room, and he buys so many gifts that we shall never be able to get them in even the Hartford house."

The Hartford house. It seemed a dream to Livy that they would ever live there again—a wonderful dream. She was tired of traveling, tired of ships and trains and hotel rooms, of public living. And she was desperately lonely for Jean and Susy.

The front door opened and Sam came in.

"Hello, darling!" Livy said. "What have you brought this time?"

"A cable," Sam said soberly. "From Katy. It just says, 'Unavoidably detained. Wait letter.'"

"Oh, no!" The cry burst from Livy. "Do you think something is wrong, Sam'l?"

"You know how Susy always is, with her head in the clouds. She probably forgot the date and wasn't ready."

"I don't think Susy would forget this date. Nothing except illness would keep her from getting on that boat," Livy said slowly, fearfully. Her heart had begun to pound but she clenched her teeth against the pain.

"Well, we will just have to wait for a letter," Sam said. He tried to sound cheerful but Livy knew him too well. Sam, too, was afraid. She looked with hatred at the slip of paper he handed her. Telegrams too often brought bad news.

The Clemenses waited eight days for the promised letter. When it came it said that Susy was ill, but the illness was not serious. She had some kind of fever but did not want a doctor, relying on friends who were mental healers. Katy wrote that she was going to insist on calling in Dr. Porter and would report to the family as soon as there was additional news.

"Susy always runs a fever easily," Clara reminded her

parents. She could not bear the anxiety on her mother's face. "If it were really serious, Katy would send a cable instead of a letter."

"I suppose so." Livy loosened the high lace collar of her dress. "Katy's reliable, and she says it is not serious —still . . . Perhaps we should pack and be ready to sail, just in case . . ."

A clock ticked loudly somewhere in the house. Sam muttered under his breath and left the room. When he came back, the clock had been silenced. He had never liked the sound of a clock and at that moment it had become unendurable.

"Shouldn't we pack, Sam'l?" she asked him.

His eyes were dark in his lined face. "Maybe, Livy. You and Clara. If you should have to sail—well, you can personally escort Susy back here with you." He glanced around the room. "While you're gone I'll look for larger quarters. Susy might need a nice big room to herself for a while." He thrust his hands into his pockets and began to whistle softly.

Livy felt as though she were watching one of Sam's fictional boy characters—Tom Sawyer or Huckleberry Finn—defiantly whistling against the ghosts of the graveyard and the dark.

"We'll pack," she said decisively, "while you send a cable and check up on the next steamer home."

He left, his gait briskly confident but his shoulders taut.

Clara was falsely cheerful as they began repacking the clothes they had unpacked only two weeks before. "I'm sure this is all waste labor," she said.

Livy scarcely heard her; she was listening for Sam's return. "Why is he taking so long?" she asked, folding and refolding a nightgown.

They heard his steps, finally, coming slowly and heavily from the entrance gate.

"I waited for an answer," he said. "It came. Katy says to wait for a cable in the morning."

Livy's lips went dry. Clara's face lost all color.

"When can we get a ship?" Livy asked.

"Tomorrow noon." Sam turned away.

Livy caught his sleeve. "Samuel—where are you going?"

"Back to the post office. I can pace the floor there as well as here—and the cable might come today."

"Mama," Clara said quietly, when her father had gone, "let's have some tea and watch the sunset from the window."

There was little sunset left. A damp breeze rustled around the hedge enclosing the yard. Far off a bird sang sleepily. A nightingale? Livy wondered, and seemed to hear Susy's adolescent voice reciting Keats: "Thou wast not born for death, immortal Bird!"

Nor Susy. Livy rocked back and forth in her chair, trying to keep her hand steady on her teacup and to smile at Clara.

It was midnight when Sam came home. At Livy's

and Clara's questioning looks, he shook his head. "No word. We may as well go to bed."

"You go, dear," Livy said. "You and Clara. I just think I'll wait up."

"I'm not tired," Sam said.

"I'm not, either," Clara insisted.

They waited, mostly silent, until after one o'clock, when Sam stood up and took Livy's hand. "You'll be sick, too, if you don't get some rest. You will need all your strength for the ocean trip."

Livy managed to doze off toward dawn. When she woke, she saw that Sam was up and dressed.

"We'll have to hurry to get the boat train," he said, sitting beside her on the bed and holding her a moment in his arms. "Oh, Livy, I dread that voyage for you. If only we'd get some word!"

"No news is good news sometimes," Livy said desperately.

After a hurried breakfast, which none of them had any appetite for, they left to catch the train to Southampton. Waiting on the platform, Livy felt catapulted back in time to last July, when they had waited at the Elmira station for the train that was to take them away from home.

The train's whistle sounded in the distance. She turned to Sam, pulling his coat collar up around his throat. "Try not to stay up so late, dear heart. Take care of yourself, for my sake if not for your own. And for Susy's."

Over Sam's shoulder, Livy saw a station attendant come toward them, waving a piece of paper.

"Mr. Clemens—cablegram, sir!"

Sam tore the message open. "Susy's recovery will be long but certain," he read, tears of relief in his eyes.

"Oh, thank God!" Livy breathed. The train was stopping beside them. "Don't worry, Youth—everything will be all right now. As soon as she's strong enough, we'll take the first boat back. I'll nurse her day and night—oh, I can't wait to see her!"

Sam gave her a tremendous hug. "On board with you," he said.

When Livy and Clara were settled in their compartment, Livy sat looking through the window, clinging to the sight of her husband. Indifferent to stares, he blew kisses to her with both hands, gesturing that some were for Clara.

The train began to move. Livy, her gloved hands clenched in her lap, wondered how she could endure the days of slow ocean travel that lay ahead of them. She wanted to clasp Susy in her arms right then.

"Are you cold, Mama?" Clara asked, looking at the figure bundled in the ship's deck chair beside her.

"A little. I'm going to go to the cabin and try to rest," Livy said. "I do want to be fresh when we see Susy."

Clara tossed her deck robe from her. "I'll go and see if there are any messages yet this morning." She prayed that there would be some good news. For almost a week now they had been on board ship, seemingly trapped in a void of sky and water that had neither beginning nor end. Depression weighed heavily on both of them.

Livy stood up. "I refuse to believe that the Pacific is the largest ocean in the world. No ocean has ever been as endless as this Atlantic." She tried to say it with a smile but her eyes were haunted.

"But it does end," Clara said. "Or our voyage does. Tomorrow! We'll be able to hug Susy and start to nurse her back to health very soon. And poor Jean—she must be feeling awful, alone to worry without us."

"Perhaps Aunt Sue went to Hartford." Susy had left Quarry Farm before she became sick, living for a time in New York and then going back to the Hartford house, from which the tenants had moved. Walking slowly toward her cabin, Livy was glad that if Susy had to be sick, it was in her own home.

The next morning Clara was hurrying along the deck toward her mother's cabin when a steward came up to her. "The captain wishes to speak to you," he said.

Frightened, Clara followed him to the captain's quarters. Waiting for her there was her father's friend Joe Twichell. He and a couple of other men had come in a tugboat to meet the ship; they had arrived the night before but had waited until morning with their sorrowful news.

Susy was dead. She had died of spinal meningitis

while Clara and her mother had been planning how
they would care for her. Twichell said that she had died
on the eighteenth of August, three days after Clara and
her mother left Southampton for home.

"Do you wish to tell your mother?" Mr. Twichell
asked Clara.

She nodded but her heart was pounding. Outside the
door of her mother's room, Clara fought for control of
her trembling limbs. How would she break the news
to Livy? What could she say that would make it any
easier?

She opened the door and found Livy awake, looking
at Clara out of eyes that seemed enormous. One look
at Clara's face told Livy what Clara could not find
words to say. Livy's face turned the color of death and
she buried it swiftly in her pillow. Clara, unable to offer
comfort because of her own grief, dropped to her knees
beside the bed and wept.

Katy Leary, who had been with Susy all the time,
was waiting for them at the Waldorf Hotel in New
York. She put her strong arms around Livy and held her
close as she described Susy's last days. Susy had paced
the floor as her father had done so often, sometimes
seizing a pen and writing incoherent messages. She imagined that she had as a companion a famous mezzo-
soprano who had died sixty years before.

"Mrs. Crane, she came down from Elmira when Susy
got really sick, and then Charley, but nothing helped.
She wouldn't take a bit of medicine from anyone but

me. I sat by her day and night." Katy went on to tell how Susy, just before she died, had put her arms around the maid's neck, rubbing Katy's cheeks with her burning hands and laying her cheek against that of the family's long-time friend. "She said, 'Mama, mama, mama!' " Katy reported brokenly.

Livy clung to Katy's hands. "Oh, if I could have been here! But how glad I am that you were able to do for her when I couldn't!"

Far away in England, Susy's father wrote out his grief and bitterness and love to Livy. "I eat—because you wish it; I go on living—because you wish it; I play billiards, & billiards, and billiards, till I am ready to drop—to keep from going mad with grief. . . . I wonder if she left any little message for me, any little mention, showing what she thought of me. I was not deserving of it, I had not earned it, but if there was any such word left behind for me, I hope it was saved up in its exact terms & that I shall get it. . . . You were the best friend she ever had, dear heart, & the steadfastest. Keep the thought of it in mind, & get from it the solace you have earned, dear Livy."

It wrung Livy's heart to know that she would have to tell Susy's father that Susy had left no message for him.

Susy Clemens was buried in Elmira beside her infant brother Langdon.

On her headstone were engraved lines by Robert

Richardson of Australia that her father had always
liked.

> *Warm summer sun, shine brightly here,*
> *Warm southern wind, blow softly here,*
> *Green sod above, lie bright, lie light,*
> *Goodnight, dear heart; good night, good night.*

Chapter Twenty

*R*ain dripped from the eaves of the house in Tedworth Square, London. Above the splash of the water came the sound of Clara's piano. The piano was seldom quiet. Clara practiced from eight in the morning until as late as ten at night. In the billiard room, Sam Clemens' pen scratched slowly, laboriously. In a large living room whose windows faced a big porch, Livy watched the rain, trying to concentrate on a shopping list for the cook.

It was November 27, 1896, her birthday and nearly three months since Susy's death. Tucked under the tatted border of a table scarf near her, its corner visible, was the note Sam had written to her.

"This is the blackest birthday you have ever seen," he had written; "may you never see its mate, dear heart."

She was fifty-one years old. Sam was sixty-one. In one of his recent moods of bitter grief, he had railed against the world tour and the necessity for making it.

"Do you remember, Livy," he asked, pacing the floor, his voice biting, "the hellish struggle it was to settle on making that lecture trip around the world? How we fought the idea, the horrible idea, the heart-torturing idea. I, almost an old man, with ill health, carbuncles, bronchitis and rheumatism. I, with patience worn to rags, I was to pack my bag and be jolted around the devil's universe for what? To pay debts that were not even of my making. And you were worried at the thought of facing such hardships of travel, and *she* was unhappy to be left alone . . .

"And as a reward, we were robbed of our greatest treasure."

Sam's words clanged in Livy's mind. She had sought for words to answer him, resorting to logic that she hoped would reach him.

"Youth, dear," she had said, "one does not act honorably for the sake of reward or even approbation."

He had looked at her swiftly, sharply, but Livy had continued bravely.

"You will not feel so bitterly when time has softened the cruelty of our blow—there must be a reason for such tragedies!"

"Well, I would like," Sam exclaimed, "just for five minutes, to understand the plan of the Creator, if He has any!"

His words had left Livy momentarily shaken. Once, such statements had seemed blasphemy to her. Now she understood them for what they were, the cry of bewilderment, frustration, and sorrow.

She could not remember what she had said. But she

knew that the conversation had ended as almost all such stormy sessions did. Rid of part of the weight of his grief, Sam had given a self-mocking smile and leaned over her, patting her head as if she were the child, his voice suddenly soft, appealing, "Don't mind anything I say, Livy. Whatever happens, you know I love you."

Livy turned from the rain. Outside Sam's billiard room study, she listened for the scratching pen. His *Joan of Arc* had been and was a success. Now he had put his faith in his newly-begun book about their world tour, *Following the Equator,* to provide the final payments to the creditors.

She could hear no sound from within the study. She imagined him sitting there, his chin in his hands, a cigar clamped fiercely between his teeth, while he struggled, like her, to control his mind and concentrate, not on the past, but on the work at hand.

The Clemens family, with Katy, spent the next four years wandering throughout Europe. Wherever they went, Sam kept writing and by the end of January, 1898, they had paid the last of their debts.

When Livy, who kept close track of their financial situation, reported to Sam that they also had a reassuring bank account, he smiled more cheerfully than he had in a long time. "Good," he said. "I reckon then I can go back to my six cent cigars." When he first went bankrupt, he had switched to cigars that sold for four cents apiece.

"And I," Livy said, "can go out and buy a gift for everyone in the household!"

With their debts paid, Sam and Livy felt that they could at last go home again. The world, especially the United States, made no secret of its pride in Mark Twain. When the news of his homecoming was circulated, he was a hero, eulogized everywhere for his brave fight against bankruptcy, misfortune, and personal sorrow.

"It's you they ought to give honor to, Livy," Sam said one evening after reading a glowing newspaper account of himself. He tossed the newspaper aside. "You are the courageous, the honorable one of this family. I never would have made it without you."

Livy touched his cheek. "We are the same, dear heart. Your honor is mine. I need no special tribute."

Because Livy had invested her personal fortune in Sam's enterprises, Mr. Rogers had insisted that the Hartford house and Sam's royalties should be placed in her name and she be considered a creditor of the bankrupt publishing firm and typesetting machine business. So now she owned the Hartford house, but none of the Clemenses wished to live there. It was too full of memories of a happier time, too full of Susy. They settled first in New York City and later at Riverdale-on-the-Hudson, going away during the summer months to various cooler or more healthful places.

In the summer of 1902, they were living in a furnished cottage at York Harbor, Maine. Clara was in

Europe, but Jean and Katy were with Sam and Livy. In early August of that year, the cluster of independent villages which made up York Harbor celebrated the 250th anniversary of the beginning of municipal, self-constituted government. Livy, who tried her best to ignore her health problems, threw herself into this event. Caught up in the color and excitement, she felt like a girl again. She visited exhibitions and watched the processions eagerly, her eyes sparkling and her cheeks pink.

A grand display of fireworks was scheduled as the finale to the celebration. As she dressed to go, Livy was aware of a grinding weariness. It would pass, she told herself. She wanted to watch the show—the scattering light of rockets arching skyward, and then drifting in tiny, flaming showers back to earth. She leaned against her bureau, remembering Fourth of July celebrations in Elmira years ago.

Her image stared back at her from the mirror. Even to herself she looked gaunt, honed, the sparkle gone. Then she saw Sam's reflection beside her own.

"Dear, dear Livy," he said. "You're tired. Too tired to go to that display." He drew her against him.

"I'm not," she protested.

"We can watch the fireworks from the piazza. We'll sit in our own chairs and have the whole effect just as well as if we were there."

"From three miles away?"

"It's a clear night. Come, Livy. It will be even more

beautiful at a distance." He touched her hair. "Give in
now, honey. Let me have my say-so this time."

She looked at him. "Am I such a dictator? Youth,
all I have ever wanted was what you wanted."

He drew her head against his shoulder. "I want you
to sit beside me on the piazza and we'll hold hands and
watch the world light up, together."

They sat as he suggested, their chairs drawn close, and
waited for the first rocket to show in the Maine sky.

"There!" Sam pointed.

A red shimmer rose above the horizon, an ethereal
fish, the bright fins and tail flashing. Almost before Livy
could see it, it vanished. Under the protection of the
light blanket Sam had spread over her, she pressed her
hand to her breast, trying to still the tumult within.
Soon she must go to bed. Sam was right; she was too
tired.

The dawn, soundless and cool, moved over the harbor. Sam Clemens dreamed that someone called him.
He stirred, turned over, and then sat up abruptly, half-
awake.

Livy was standing on the other side of the room, her
nightgown silver in the morning light. She was leaning
against the wall, panting.

"Sam'l—I can't breathe!"

He leaped from bed and ran to her. "Livy!" He half-
carried, half-helped her back to the bed. "Lie there, I'll
get a doctor. Lie still, dearest. Please lie still."

Katy, aroused by the commotion, appeared in the hall as Sam rushed toward the telephone.

"Take care of her, Katy!" he said.

Katy hurried in to her mistress. She combed her fingers through Livy's hair, gently, murmuring, "It'll be all right, dearie. You overdid, maybe, but you'll be as good as new soon."

Livy looked up at her. "It's August," she said. "August the twelfth."

Tears came to Katy's eyes. Six years from the day Susy was to have met the family in Europe. "You ought to forget that now," she said to Livy.

The heart attack Livy suffered that night was very severe. Clara came home from Europe and Sue Crane from Elmira. When Livy was strong enough to be moved, the family returned to Riverdale-on-the-Hudson where Livy was once more confined to bed. No visitors and none of the family were permitted to see her except Clara, as the assistant nurse, and Sam for a few minutes each day.

Livy, looking through the windows of her room at the wide expanse of sky and the topmost branches of trees, waited as patiently as she could for Sam's daily visit. She knew that he stood outside her door long before the moment arrived, as impatient as she was. For the first weeks of her illness, she had not been allowed to see him at all—she had had to live on the notes he sent in to her by Clara or the nurse.

"Don't know the date nor day," one of these notes

had read. "But, anyway, it is a soft and pensive foggy morning, Livy darling, and the naked tree branches are tear-beaded, and Nature has the look of trying to keep from breaking down and sobbing, poor old thing. Good morning, dear heart, I love you dearly. 'Y.' "

Another note: "Dearest, we've had a grand dispute as to when Clara was first able to read, either German or English—and of course I was right and of course I was put down by the strong hand. I will not stay here, I am going to heaven. There they will not abuse me, but will praise me and pet me and flatter me and give me a halo, and I am not going to lend it to the children. Good-night, my darling—*you* shall wear it sometimes."

There was one sound that Livy missed acutely and that was the scratch of Sam's pen. And the noises he made while writing—the coughs, occasional groans and sighs. She knew he was writing short stories and articles, but when she could not hear him, it was as if he were doing his work on another planet.

She sent him a note. "Youth my own precious Darling," she wrote, "I feel so frightfully banished. Couldn't you write in my boudoir? Then I could hear you clear your throat and it would be such joy to feel you near. . . . I miss you sadly, sadly. 'Your Livy.' "

Happily, Sam moved his writing equipment to the boudoir which adjoined Livy's bedroom. He coughed often for her benefit, hummed, rattled papers unnecessarily, and wondered if he was not becoming the noisiest author-at-work in the United States. When, however, he went a step farther and began to speak to Livy through the closed door between the rooms, Livy's nurse banished him. He was exciting Mrs. Clemens too much, she said.

Sam went back to communicating with Livy by notes. Clara brought Livy news of the world and herself and Jean. Ossip Gabrilowitsch, a brilliant young musician Clara had met in Vienna, had arrived in Riverdale, and Clara had promised to marry him, she told her mother.

Slowly, Livy's health improved. As it did, she began to take charge of the household once more. Sam was growing too fond of spending his mornings in bed reading or writing, a habit which Livy believed would weaken him physically. She sent him messages suggesting that he would feel better if he would get up at a reasonable hour and take a walk.

If only Livy herself would be able to walk even a few steps again, Sam thought, he would walk around the earth every morning before breakfast.

The doctors recommended a warmer climate for Livy, so the next October, when she was stronger, the Clemens family, with Katy; the nurse, Margaret Sherry; and Sam's new private secretary, Isabelle Lyon, sailed for Europe. Again they rented a villa in Florence which had a long terrace adjoining Livy's quarters. There, in a little parlor, she and Sam luxuriated in the warmth, the scent of roses, and the flowering orange trees. For a while Livy was better, but with the coming of winter she suffered several setbacks.

Clara was taking voice lessons in Florence and in the spring she made her singing debut, receiving high praise.

"She and Gabrilowitsch will make a real concert pair," Sam said, after the concert. Both he and Livy thought wistfully, for a moment, of Susy's dream of just such a career as Clara was now launched on.

"I'm so glad," Livy said, "for dear Clara." But she looked worn and exhausted.

Sam felt a chill go through him. "You must lie down now, darling. You have been too excited about the debut. I'll come back to see you later." He called the nurse and left Livy to rest.

By May, however, Livy was again well enough to be taken out in a wheelchair onto the terrace.

"Oh, Katy, how beautiful everything looks this time of the year!" Livy cried, glancing at the newly blooming roses as red as curled fire. "I do hope Sam'l finds us a villa that will have roses." Sam, with Jean, had been trying to find a house they could buy, in Florence.

On the fifth of June, Sam found the house and he and Jean hurried home to tell the rest of the household.

That evening, at seven o'clock, as Sam sat by Livy's bedside, he was startled to see how young she looked. Her face was radiant. She was full of enthusiasm over his description of the villa he had found and insisted on seeing the plans for fixing it.

"I'll buy it tomorrow," Sam told her. "And we'll move you to it the minute you can bear the journey."

There was a moment's hesitation. Then Livy said, "I want you to buy it—only, Youth, you must not be disappointed if we can't move too soon. I'll be content here, if we have to stay."

He was afraid she was growing depressed again and sought for words to cheer her. But she shook off the somber mood by herself and began to trace a fragile finger over the house plans.

Sam knew that he was overstaying the fifteen minutes allotted to him, but he could not move. It was too wonderful to have Livy like her old self. When a half-hour had passed, he said:

"Livy, darling, I must go. I am tiring you."

"Don't go!" She put her hands against his face, caressing his cheeks. "Stay. I get so lonely for you. And we have a new home to think about." She talked on animatedly, clinging to him, seemingly unable to stop. Sam was torn between joy in her good spirits and fear that she was overdoing.

At last he made himself stand up and go toward the door.

"You will come back?" she asked.

"Yes," he promised. "At half-past nine to say goodnight."

He stood in the doorway, throwing kisses, his heart swelling with love as she returned them, her new-found smile still brightening her face.

Sam went to his room, so exalted he could not sit still. He walked around aimlessly and then went upstairs to the room which held the piano. He had scarcely touched a piano since Susy died.

He sat down, letting his hands lie motionless on the keys for a moment. He cleared his throat, sought for the proper notes, and began to sing loud and clear, for Livy. As he sang, the years dropped away and he was back in the Langdon home, Livy beside him in the lamplight, shy and frail but unimaginably beautiful. Above his singing, he heard the ringing of church bells, then the sound of Jean's footsteps climbing the stairs and coming in to sit beside him, quietly, listening.

From her room, Livy heard. Louder and nearer than the church bells observing the Forty Hours' Adoration, came the voice she knew so well:

> *My Lord He call me!*
> *He call me out of thunder!*

She said to the nurse, "He is singing a goodnight to me."

Miss Sherry smiled. "Mr. Clemens has a pleasant voice."

Much more than pleasant, Livy thought dreamily. It was distinguished, like everything else about her Sam'l. She closed her eyes, remembering how often he had sung when the children were little. She felt the ring on her finger. It was too large now, but age had given it an added sheen. Thirty-three and a half years of marriage, love, work, companionship, through happiness and sorrow. She felt deeply grateful.

That evening, June 5, 1904, at a quarter past nine, Livy Clemens died.

Two weeks later, the family sailed for America, taking Livy home to be buried in Elmira beside her parents and Susy and the little son, Langdon, whom she had lost such a long time before.

Livy was liked by almost everyone who knew her but to her husband and children she was almost a saint. Mark Twain wrote to a friend, after her death: "The family's relation to her was peculiar & unusual, & could not exist toward another. Our love for her was the ordinary love, but added to it was a reverent & quite conscious worship. Perhaps it was nearly like a subject's feeling for his sovereign—a something which he does not have to reason out, or nurse, or study about, but which comes natural. It was an influence which proceeded from the grace, & purity, & sweetness, & simplicity, & charity, & magnanimity & dignity of her character." This attitude, Sam went on to say, was also the attitude of servants, shopgirls, postmen, and others who had known her.

In a tender tribute to her, *Eve's Diary*, written not long after Livy's death, Mark Twain said in one sentence all that his wife had meant to him:

"Wheresoever she was, there was Eden."

Acknowledgments

The authors wish to thank Mr. Fred Anderson of the Mark Twain Library at the University of California, Berkeley, California; Dr. Ida Langdon, Elmira, New York; and the Chemung County Historical Center, for their cooperation in assisting the authors in their research.

For permission to quote, grateful acknowledgment is made to The Citadel Press, the Henry E. Huntington Library and Art Gallery, Harcourt, Brace & World, Inc., and Harper & Row, Publishers, Incorporated, The Mark Twain Company.

From *Mark Twain, Family Man* by Caroline T. Harnsberger. The Citadel Press, New York, N. Y.

From *Mark Twain to Mrs. Fairbanks*, edited by Dixon Wecter. Henry E. Huntington Library and Art Gallery.

From *A Lifetime with Mark Twain* by Mary Lawton. Harcourt, Brace & World, Inc.

From *A Short Life of Mark Twain* by Albert Bigelow Paine. Copyright, 1920, by Harper & Row, Publishers, Incorporated. Pages 148, 170.

From *My Father Mark Twain* by Clara Clemens. Copyright, 1931, by Clara Clemens Gabrilowitsch. Reprinted by permission of Harper & Row, Publishers, Incorporated. Pages 156, 171, 172, 173, 175, 178.

From *Love Letters of Mark Twain,* edited by Dixon Wecter. Copyright 1947, 1949, by The Mark Twain Company. Pages 48, 75, 76, 84, 120, 183.

From *Autobiography of Mark Twain,* edited by Charles Neider. Harper & Row, Publishers, Incorporated. Pages 64, 115, 116, 117, 181.

From *Biography of Mark Twain* by Albert Bigelow Paine. Harper & Row, Publishers, Incorporated. Pages 118, 123, 134.

From *Eve's Diary* by Mark Twain. Harper & Row, Publishers, Incorporated. Page 183.

From *The Prince and the Pauper* by Mark Twain. Harper & Row, Publishers, Incorporated. Page 94.

From "A Record of the Small Foolishnesses of Susie and Bay Clemens" by Mark Twain. Dialogue on page 93, lines 4, 16 and page 94, lines 16, 19, copyright, 1963, The Mark Twain Company.

For the use of original sources for research, grateful acknowledgment is made to the Mark Twain Library, University of California; Yale University Library; Alderman Library, University of Virginia; The Mark Twain Company for previously unpublished quotations from the writings of the Clemens family (Copyright, 1963).

INDEX

INDEX